ASTRONOMY: A BRIEF INTRODUCTION

WALTER H. HESSE
California State Polytechnic College
Pomona, California

ASTRONOMY: A BRIEF INTRODUCTION

ADDISON-WESLEY
PUBLISHING COMPANY
READING, MASSACHUSETTS
PALO ALTO · LONDON · DON MILLS, ONTARIO

This book is in the
ADDISON-WESLEY SERIES IN EARTH SCIENCES

PREFACE

This book was written for the nonscience student who is more concerned with the historical and cultural impact of science on society than with its technical aspects.

Astronomy is an ancient science, perhaps the oldest of the physical sciences, and its development has had a profound effect on the thinking of man not only in science but in philosophy, religion, and the social sciences as well. The intention of this book is to show how man, for many centuries, has viewed his physical environment, how changes in these views have taken place, and how it is only in the past few decades that man has begun to understand the nature of the universe.

This book is intended for a one-quarter survey course in astronomy or for supplementary material in a one-year physical science course. References are included at the end of each chapter to provide supplementary material. Problems and techniques are described to illustrate how man's thinking has enabled him to utilize the tools at hand to solve profound problems.

The historical treatment in the first chapter is brief, accentuating the high points in man's changing view of the universe from an earth-centered to a sun-centered universe to a universe for which a center cannot be defined. The second chapter deals with light and the instrumentation used to gather and analyze it for the purpose of studying distant objects. Following this is a discussion of the solar system: its constituent parts and its organization. The fourth chapter deals with the properties of stars, and the fifth chapter deals with the organization of stars into galaxies and the arrangement of the galaxies in the universe. The sixth chapter presents theories that have been suggested to explain the formation of the universe and the prospect of there being life in regions of the universe other than the solar system.

It is, of course, impossible to cover all aspects of astronomy in a single text, and no attempt has been made to do so. This survey is written to serve as a guide. It is left to the instructor to fill in those areas that he deems important.

W.H.H.

Pomona, California
April, 1967

CONTENTS

CHAPTER 1

INTRODUCTION TO ASTRONOMY

From the beginning, man has viewed the heavens and wondered. He has seen the cycle of change repeated endlessly, and he has speculated on the nature of his celestial environment. Gradually theories evolved to explain these changes, giving rise to astronomy, the "science of stars."

Astronomy is concerned with the study of the universe, particularly the solar system, all the stars and galaxies visible with the aid of the most powerful telescopes, and the vast spaces in between. Astronomy is one of the oldest sciences. Carvings on ancient tablets show that it attracted the attention of people at least 5000 years ago.

1.1 ANCIENT ASTRONOMY

Chinese astronomers, held in very high esteem by their emperors, made many celestial observations in the far distant past. They were capable of predicting the occurrence of eclipses twenty-two centuries B.C., and recognized the value of the polar star as a means of orientation. The exact position of the polar star was used to align all the important public buildings and temples in China in an exact north-south direction. The front door of each house, as well as the emperor's throne, was made to face exactly south. The Chinese made use of astronomical observations to develop a calendar and, 2000 years before Christ, they determined that the year was 365 days long.

The Egyptians also used astronomical observations to determine position and to measure the passage of time. Pyramids and temples were carefully oriented with respect to certain important celestial bodies. The steep shaftlike entrance to the Pyramid of Cheops was pointed directly at the celestial pole. Temples in Egypt were built to permit the star Sirius to shine directly into their entrances at dawn in the spring, thus signaling the advent of the annual Nile flood.

The Babylonians were even more astronomy-minded than the Egyptians. They left many records of observations of eclipses and the movements of comets and other celestial bodies. The Babylonians also developed star pictures that served as maps for the location of stars in the sky. The Greeks, Chinese, and Arabs did the same, and the Romans adopted the Greek star pictures which, in turn, were passed on to us. These groups of stars were called *constellations* from a Latin word meaning "stars grouped together."

The Babylonians noted that several celestial bodies, including the sun and the moon, had motions which were more complex than the motion of the fixed stars. The Greeks called these bodies planets, *planetes,* meaning "wanderers," because their paths seemed to wander against the background of the fixed stars. The Babylonian astronomers became quite adept at predicting the movement of heavenly bodies and could foretell an eclipse. This made them powerful as forecasters of the future, and the study of the heavens began to take on religious significance. Many myths arose related to the constellations. Good and bad luck was ascribed to events in the sky, and the positions of the planets were thought to influence the course of destiny.

The keeping of records on the movement of celestial bodies was difficult for ordinary men and fell to the priests skilled in the art of practical astronomy. The sun, a source of light and warmth, necessary for the successful growth of crops, was worshiped by many early civilizations. The astronomer-priest became an important personage, and his proficiency in observing, recording, and predicting the occurrence of astronomical phenomena was a beginning of intellectual pursuits.

The Greeks began to adopt the Babylonian astronomy around 600 B.C., and although some myths and astrological dogma remained, much usable knowledge was carried over. Here, perhaps, was the end of what may be considered the first stage in the history of astronomy. Myth and magic relating to astronomical phenomena were gradually replaced by an approach which sought for answers by the use of mathematics and physics.

1.2   EARLY DEVELOPMENT OF THE HELIOCENTRIC THEORY

One of the early Greek astronomers was Pythagorus of Samos, born in approximately 590 B.C. He was the founder of the Pythagorean Brotherhood, a religious order devoted to mathematical and religious contemplation. The Pythagoreans devised the astronomical system of planets in perfect circular orbits in the celestial sphere. In this system, the sun, the moon, and five visible planets were thought to move around the earth from west to east at varying speeds, suggesting varying distances. Pythagorus himself, in 525 B.C., first suggested that the earth was a sphere, for reasons of harmony with the circular concept of the universe and because of the curvature of the earth's shadow on the moon during an eclipse.

Because motions not consistent with the harmonious arrangement of the universe were observed, there arose several schools of thought about the exact position of the earth in the universe. Some Pythagoreans objected to certain aspects of the scheme, namely, that the planets moved from west to east at different speeds while simultaneously rotating in the opposite direction every 24 hours. Philolaus, in approximately 450 B.C., conceived the idea that the earth traveled from west to east around a "central fire." One side of the earth constantly faced this fire, this side being opposite that on which Greece was located. The central fire, considered by Philolaus as the center of the universe, was hidden from the earth by a "counter earth" which kept pace with the earth as it moved in its orbit. This interpretation accounted for the daily movement of the stars and placed the earth with the other planets in a west-to-east orbit around a common center. However, several objections to this explanation were immediately raised. If the earth and the moon revolved around a common center, then the distance between the earth and the moon should vary considerably during a 24-hour period, resulting in a marked change in the apparent diameter of the moon. Also, it was asked, would not the distant stars show a parallactic displacement as a result of the earth's orbit around the central fire? The answer was that the diameter of the earth's orbit was very small, too small to appreciably change the apparent diameter of the moon, and that the stars were too distant for parallax to be observable.

Heraclides of Pontus, in about 350 B.C., attempted to further eliminate objections to Philolaus' design by proposing that the earth rotated on its axis. Heraclides also grappled with another imperfection in the orderly Pythagorean scheme. Mercury and Venus always remained close to the sun and were never seen traveling across the night sky as other planets were. Heraclides proposed the idea that these planets orbited the sun, suggesting that the earth was not the center around which all other planets traveled.

This direction of thought was followed by Aristarchus of Samos, an astronomer in about 280 B.C., who concluded that the sun and the fixed stars were immovable and that the earth and the planets revolved around the sun. Aristarchus had more difficulty in justifying his concept than Philolaus did, because Aristarchus placed the earth third from the sun. This was a much greater distance from the center of the universe than the distance proposed by Philolaus, and it was therefore more subject to the test of parallactic displacement of the stars. The fact that this test failed was not to Aristarchus' discredit but, rather, was due to the lack of instruments of sufficient accuracy to measure the extremely small parallax that did occur. Thus the heliocentric theory was received with little enthusiasm and lay dormant for more than seventeen centuries before it was revived by Copernicus.

Fig. 1.1 The geocentric scheme of the universe as devised by the ancient Greeks. Only one sphere is shown here for simplicity. The earth occupied the center and it was composed of the four elements, earth, water, air, and fire. Surrounding this were the spheres of the moon, Mercury, Venus, the sun, Mars, Jupiter, Saturn, and the outer shell of the stars. [From the DeGolyer copy of Petrus Apianus' *Cosmographie*, 1551.]

1.3   DEVELOPMENT OF THE GEOCENTRIC THEORY

Aristarchus' work was the culmination of one school of thought in Greek astronomy, inspired by the work of Pythagorus. The proponents of this line of thought attempted to organize an arrangement of planets which would permit the observable motions to be explained in the simplest manner.

Plato (427?–347 B.C.), took an entirely different approach. He accepted the Pythagorean view that the earth was the center of the universe and held that the heavenly bodies, whose motions were uniform and circular, were perfect in nature (Fig. 1.1). He charged his students with the task of finding perfect circular motions that would explain the apparent and somewhat irregular movements of the planets. Eudoxus, in about 370 B.C., accepted his teacher's assignment and devised a system in which each planet was attached to a series of concentric spheres, and each sphere rotated on its axis in a manner providing the planet with its apparent movements (Fig. 1.2). This system required three spheres for both the sun and the moon, four spheres for each of the five planets and one sphere to account for the daily rotation of the stars. Eudoxus' pupil Callipus refined this system slightly to improve its accuracy by adding an extra sphere for the sun, the moon, and the five planets, making a total of thirty-four spheres. This system imitated the observed motions of the planets and preserved the Pythagorean universe intact. It was simple and conformed to the existing design, as required by Plato.

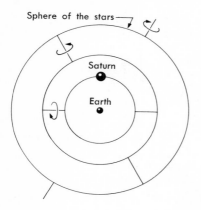

Sphere of the stars

Saturn

Earth

◀ **Fig. 1.2**   Concentric spheres were used to account for the observed motion of a planet. [*From Holton and Roller, Foundations of Modern Physical Science,* 1958.]

Fig. 1.3   The apparent eccentric motion of the sun S (or planet) as viewed from the earth results because the sun rotates at a uniform distance from center O which is offset from the stationary earth at E. An observer on earth would see the sun closer to the earth in winter and farther away in summer. ▶

Fig. 1.4   In epicyclic motion, the planet P revolves around point D which, in turn, revolves, at a uniform distance around the stationary earth at the center. ▶

Aristotle (384–322 B.C.) perhaps the foremost scholar in Greek culture, did much to influence thinking in favor of the geocentric or earth-centered idea of the universe. He made no basic change in the arrangement but, rather, changed the concept of the system. Eudoxus had viewed his scheme as a purely geometric construction. Aristotle was responsible for the notion that the spheres were real physical entities. He added a number of "unrolling spheres" to the system between the existing sets of spheres carrying each planet. These "unrolling spheres" rotated in a direction opposite to the spheres controlling planetary movement, and thus prevented the movements of one planet from being carried over to the movements of the next. The entire system, with its fifty-five spheres, according to Aristotle, was moved by the *primum mobile,* or prime mover, located at the edge of the universe. Each group of spheres was controlled by a lesser mover, moving the planets in a west-to-east direction opposite to that of the prime mover. For this reason the inner planets moved rapidly while the outer planets moved slowly, because they were influenced to a greater extent by the prime mover. Aristotle maintained that the earth was the center of the universe and, furthermore, that the earth was spherical in shape, small, and entirely motionless.

Aristotle's reasons for claiming that the earth was a sphere were quite sound, stemming from both observational and theoretical considerations. He used the same argument that Pythagorus used, namely, that the shadow of the earth on the moon during an eclipse was circular. He found that objects disappeared below the horizon he was traveling away from and that new objects appeared above the horizon he was moving toward.

This was particularly noticeable with respect to the position of constellations when he was traveling north or south. Aristotle also considered that the sphere was symmetrically perfect, and that therefore the earth, to conform to the perfect symmetry of the universe, had to be a sphere.

Aristotle's tremendous influence as a teacher was principally responsible for fixing the geocentric as the acceptable theory of the universe for almost 2000 years. He wrote extensively on scientific subjects and discussed the problems of scientific philosophy. In the latter instance, Aristotle would make a distinction between a scheme devised to save a particular theory, and a theory based on true physical causes. Unfortunately, in the case of the geocentric theory, it would appear that Aristotle subscribed to the former of these two choices.

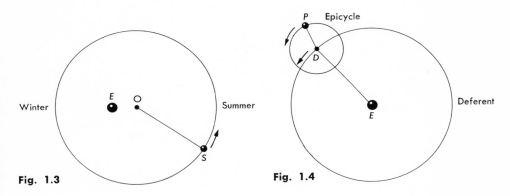

Fig. 1.3   **Fig. 1.4**

While the Aristotelian concept of the universe was the basic one for centuries, some criticisms did arise, bringing about the need for further modifications. This system did not account for the fact that some of the planets at times appeared to be near the earth and at other times appeared to be farther away. For example, it was found that the sun appeared slightly larger in the winter (and therefore closer to the earth) and smaller in the summer. Hipparchus of Rhodes in the second century B.C., and Claudius Ptolemy of Alexandria in the second century A.D., must receive credit for devising a system of *eccentrics* and *epicycles* which accounted for the inconsistencies and at the same time preserved the geocentric theory.

The uneven motion of the sun was explained in another way by assuming that the sun moved at a uniform speed around a circular path, but that the earth was located a short distance from the center of the sun's orbit. This would cause the sun to approach the earth at a slightly increased speed during the winter, and to recede from the earth at a slightly slower speed during the summer (Fig. 1.3). Removing the earth from the center of the system was not in keeping with the symmetrical scheme of the universe, but the observed motions required an adjustment of this kind.

Another system of motion which produced the same results placed the earth at the center of a main circle, *the deferent,* while a small circle, *the epicycle,* described the path of the planet as it went around the main circle (Fig. 1.4). The planet, in effect, was undergoing two motions simultaneously: one around the point *D,* or epicycle, while the point *D* was moving around the main circle, or deferent. This system of motion would permit the earth to be at the center of the universe. However, it removed the planets from the rigid spheres into which they had been placed by the Aristotelian system.

An advantage of the use of epicycles was that it permitted an explanation of *retrograde motion*. Certain of the planets slowed down and for a short period of time reversed their course of direction against the background of stationary stars before continuing their normal motion. This made the planets appear to exhibit a looplike movement as they traveled along their paths (Fig. 1.5).

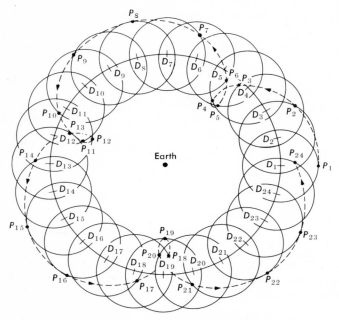

Fig. 1.5   Retrograde motion occurring during a planet's orbit is accounted for by use of epicycles. [From Holton and Roller, *Foundations of Modern Physical Science*, 1958.]

The use of eccentrics and epicycles did not completely satisfy the requirements of celestial motion. Ptolemy found it necessary to introduce still another device, known as the *equant*. To represent the motion of some planets it was necessary to show O as the center, with the earth E set off center, and the equant Q an equal distance on the other side of the earth (Fig. 1.6). This complex arrangement worked very satisfactorily in that it permitted accurate determination of planetary positions for the future or for the past.

Ptolemy's system was based on complex mathematics and was simply a device for explaining and predicting planetary motion. His system, which to him had no physical reality, replaced the complexity of solid spheres so important to the Aristotelian concept. Ptolemy did retain the basic features of the geocentric theory, namely, a stationary spherical earth in the center of a spherical universe in which certain bodies moved at uniform speeds in a circular manner. By using eccentrics, epicycles, and equants, he developed a system which endured for almost 1400 years. Ptolemy recorded all this in a monumental work, the *Almagest,* which became the one authoritative work until the sixteenth century. During this period the work was translated into Latin, Arabic, and back into Latin when it was reintroduced to Europe. Corrections were made to conform with the current thinking of the translators. Gradually, men again invested the mechanism with a physical property by considering the eccentrics and epicycles as part of a number of crystal spheres.

It was Dante in the fourteenth century who described the system as a series of concentric spheres with the stationary earth at the center. The earth, made up of the four elements, earth, water, fire, and air as prescribed by Aristotle, was surrounded by ten skies or spheres. The spheres nearest the earth contained the moon. The next six spheres contained the sun and the planets, and the eighth sphere contained the stars. The ninth sphere was invisible, but must exist, they reasoned, because it was the *primum mobile* or prime mover responsible for the movement of all the other spheres. The tenth sphere was the *empyrean heaven,* the house of God, and this sphere was at rest. Thus the Aristotelian concept of the universe continued to dominate cosmologial thinking during the Middle Ages and the Renaissance. It was this concept that Copernicus challenged in the early sixteenth century at what may be considered the end of the second stage in astronomical history.

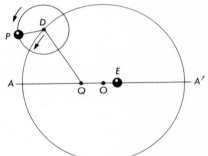

Fig. 1.6 Motion of a planet *P* as it revolves around *D* which moves around the orbit with respect to the equant at *Q*. The planet maintains circular motion with respect to *O* and uniform motion as seen from *Q*. [From Holton and Roller, *Foundations of Modern Physical Science,* 1958.]

1.4 A RETURN TO THE HELIOCENTRIC THEORY

Niklas Koppernigk, or Copernicus—to use the Latinized form—(1473–1543), was born in Poland into an era of great change and was a contemporary of such men as Columbus, da Vinci, and Michelangelo. His father died when Copernicus was ten years old and the boy went to live with his uncle who planned a career in the church for him. Copernicus studied at the University of Cracow where he became interested in astronomy and mathematics, and in 1496 he went to Italy to study medicine and law. He pursued his interest in astronomy while in Italy, where he thought at great length about the need for improving the Ptolemaic system. When his uncle died in 1512, Copernicus assumed the duties as Canon of Frauenberg, an appointment he had received during his stay in Italy. For the next 30 years he carried on the many duties connected with his office, but during this time he was primarily concerned with the details of his new planetary system.

To say that Copernicus set the world on its ear, in a literal sense, is true but that he did so can be seen only in retrospect. This was not his intention. Copernicus was, in a sense, following Plato's admonition to his students to find a system which would provide the simplest perfect statement of motion to describe the Pythagorean arrangement of the universe. He studied the works of Ptolemy at great length, and he found that errors, which had supposedly been corrected or accounted for were reoccurring. This, he felt, was not in keeping with the supposed orderliness of nature. Copernicus also objected to the frequent need of the equant as a means of providing the planets with uniform circular motion. He felt that ". . . a system of this sort seemed neither sufficiently absolute nor sufficiently pleasing to the mind." At the same time Copernicus was of the opinion that any motion other than a uniform circular motion was impossible. Referring to the classical works, he found that a number of thinkers in the past, such as Philolaus and Heraclides, had suggested that the earth did move. He must have reasoned that motion results regardless of whether the object being observed moves, or the observer moves with respect to the object.

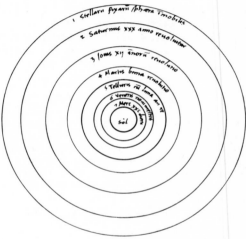

Fig. 1.7 The Copernican concept of the heliocentric system. The epicycles used in the system are omitted. [From Copernicus' *De Revolutionibus*, 1543.]

By making observations and calculations of his own, Copernicus found that all observed celestial movements could be accounted for by substituting the sun for the earth at the center of the system (Fig. 1.7). In this way, the system was notably simplified in keeping with the orderly nature of the universe. At the same time, the Pythagorean concept, that the motions of the heavenly bodies were circular and uniform, had been preserved. His system with the stationary sun at the center consisted of the planets arranged in the order of their periods of revolution. Mercury, revolving around the sun with the shortest period, is closest to the sun while Saturn, with the longest period, is the farthest planet from the sun. Surrounding this, and at a great distance, is an immobile sphere containing all the stars. The motion attributed to this sphere by the Ptolemaic system is now seen as the result of the earth's rotation on its axis.

George Joachim, better known by his Latin name Rheticus, gave an analogy which aptly described the simplicity of movement of the earth around the sun as prescribed by his friend Copernicus.

"Since we see that this one motion of the earth satisfies an almost infinite number of appearances, should we not attribute to God, the Creator of nature, that skill which we observe in the common makers of clocks? For they carefully avoid inserting in the mechanism any superfluous wheel, or any whose function could be served better by another with a slight change of position."

Copernicus himself, for purely aesthetic reasons, may have felt the need for a sun-centered system. In his description of the system he writes of the sun:

"In the midst of all dwells the immovable sun. For who, indeed, in this magnificent temple would place the giver of life in any place other than where it can illuminate all parts at the same time? . . . And so the sun reposing as if on a throne rules the family of planets which surrounds him . . ."

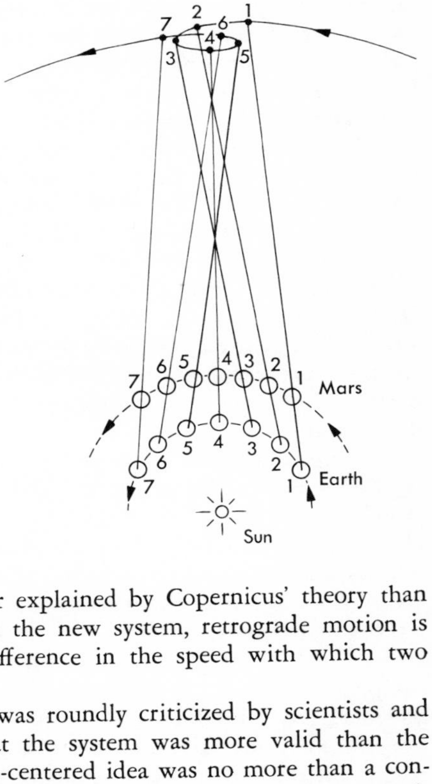

Fig. 1.8 Retrograde motion, an apparent motion, is the result of the difference in the orbital speed of the planet. [From Holton and Roller, *Foundations of Physical Science,* 1958.]

The nature of retrograde motion was also better explained by Copernicus' theory than by the use of epicycles, previously discussed. In the new system, retrograde motion is only an apparent motion resulting from the difference in the speed with which two planets travel around the sun (Fig. 1.8).

For all its simplicity, the Copernican system was roundly criticized by scientists and religious leaders alike. He offered no proof that the system was more valid than the Ptolemaic system, and it was argued that the sun-centered idea was no more than a convenient mathematical device for use in astronomical calculations. It appeared that man's ego was such that he demanded the center of the universe as the place for his earth: to abandon the geocentric theory was philosophically impossible. Another objection to placing the earth in its new position was Copernicus' inability to exhibit a parallactic displacement of the stars despite the earth's supposedly greater orbit. His explanation of the immense distance to the fixed stars was not acceptable to man, who could not imagine such a distant heaven while hell was so close underfoot.

Still another argument against the theory of a rotating earth was that centrifugal force would cause the earth to fly apart. Copernicus countered that the much vaster sphere holding the fixed stars would be more susceptible to disintegration by such a force. This answer was not satisfactory within the framework of the Aristotelian thinking which prevailed at that time. The skies were considered to be made up of the quintessence, a perfect and weightless substance not affected by any earthly physical force such as centrifugal force. In addition, it was argued, if the earth rotated, objects thrown into the air would be left behind. It was obvious to everyone that this did not occur, nor did the air rush by as a high wind due to the earth's rotation. To this Copernicus replied that the air rotated with the earth, being contiguous to and a part of the earth.

Copernicus did not completely abandon Ptolemy. He still maintained that the paths of the planets about the sun were perfect circles and a few epicycles were required in the calculations in order to accommodate all the observed movements. Copernicus could offer no proof that his system was true and that the Ptolemaic system was false, but was merely able to present his system as a more convenient one. Copernicus presented his hypotheses and findings in a work which bore the imposing title *Nicolai Copernici Torimensis de Revolutionibis Orbium Coelesium, Libri VI,* which he dedicated to Pope Paul III. The first copy was placed in Copernicus' hands a few hours before his death in 1543. Thus the world was presented the heliocentric theory. Because Copernicus was the first to calculate the mathematical basis for this theory, it became known as the *Copernican system* although it did not originate with him.

The Copernican system nevertheless was of great importance since it eventually provided a means of explaining other phenomena such as tidal action and the occurrence of tradewinds, and did much to revitalize and stimulate scientific thought in the sixteenth century. It may be that if a date needs to be specified for the beginning of modern science, 1543 would do well. With the presentation of the heliocentric theory a new stimulus was given to scientific thought which eventually culminated in the Scientific Revolution.

The precision in observations which Copernicus was unable to achieve was realized by Tycho Brahe. Tycho Brahe (1546–1601), born in Denmark of noble parentage, abandoned the life of hounds and horses in favor of academic pursuits in astronomy. As a boy, he was inspired by the ability of astronomers to predict the occurrence of eclipses and exclaimed, "To know of such a thing in advance makes a man almost a god!" After studying mathematics and astronomy at Swiss and German universities, he was appointed court astrologer to the Danish King Frederick II and made governor of Hven, an island in the Baltic Sea. Here, at the King's expense, he set up an observatory equipped with elaborate instruments, with which he was able to make observations with an accuracy never before achieved. He set out with the avowed purpose of proving the Copernican theory false and of revising and improving the precision of the Ptolemaic theory. In the process he developed his Tychonian geostatic system which had all the planets circling around the sun and this system revolving around the earth. Tycho Brahe's achievements were not in the realm of theoretical astronomy but in the extremely accurate observations that he made of the planets and the stars. He recorded the data meticulously, and in 1592 he published a catalog of 777 stars, which became a standard reference for that time.

One of the achievements of Tycho Brahe's life was the discovery in November, 1572, of a new star located in the constellation of Cassiopeia. It was an extremely bright object rivaling Venus in brilliance and under ideal conditions visible even in the daytime. Brahe did not think this discovery unique: he cited a similar discovery by Hipparchus ". . . a star different from all others previously seen, one born in his own age . . ." Brahe felt this to be a star on the celestial sphere and not one of the planets. Nor did he consider it to be permanent ". . . for anything that rises after the completion of the Creator can only be transitory." In this, Brahe was correct, for the star began to fade and in 18 months had disappeared entirely.

After the death of his royal patron, Brahe left Denmark because of a quarrel with his patron's successor. He entered the service of Emperor Rudolph II in Prague and was joined there by Johannes Kepler. Thus in the year 1600, two forces were joined which were to profoundly affect astronomy and science in general. Tycho Brahe, the brilliant observer, and Johannes Kepler, the mathematician and theorizer, combined their considerable complementary talents.

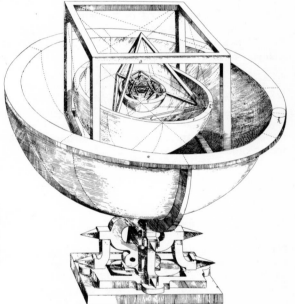

Fig. 1.9 Planets are spaced by placing the five Pythagorean figures between the spheres of the six planets. [From Holton and Roller, *Foundations of Modern Physical Science,* 1958.]

Johannes Kepler (1571–1630) was convinced of the validity of the Copernican theory while a student at Tübingen and became dedicated to the proposition that this described the true structure of the universe. Kepler's first attempt to present his theory was recorded in 1596 in his *Mysterium Cosmographicum* (*Mysterious Universe*), where he describes a model of the universe fitting the five Pythagorean figures between the spheres of the six planets. The five Pythagorean figures, the cube, tetrahedron, dodecahedron, icosahedron, and octahedron, were recognized in antiquity as the only solid figures possible with identical faces and with faces that were all equilateral. He found that the relative spacing that resulted by placing the five classical geometric figures one inside the other corresponded quite closely to the observed relative distances between the planets (Fig. 1.9). Kepler felt that the discrepancies that did occur were due to errors in observation. By association with Tycho Brahe, he hoped to obtain the best data available to test his hypothesis.

Kepler had complete faith in the observations he obtained from Brahe but was soon to find that the extensive data on the planet Mars could not be made to fit the uniform circular motion of the Copernican system. There was a difference of eight minutes of arc between the data and a perfect circle, which could not be accounted for by observational error. After about four years of tedious work, Kepler conceived the idea of an ovoid or egg-shaped orbit for Mars. He made many more measurements and calculations, but to no avail. The egg-shaped orbit was too narrow by about as much as the circle was too large. He felt that the true answer must be somewhere in between. He eventually solved the problem by fitting the orbit to an ellipse. To reach this conclusion, Kepler first came to the realization, also recognized by Copernicus, that the planets did not orbit the sun but, rather, a point offset from the sun. Following this line of reasoning, he was able to ascertain that the planets did not go around in their orbits at uniform speed but, rather, slowed down when farthest away from the sun (*aphelion*) and speeded up when closest to the sun (*perihelion*). This led to the formulation of his Second Law of Motion and did away with the sacred ideas of *uniform motions* for the planets. More tedious and frustrating work finally led him to the conclusion that all the planets followed elliptical orbits. Kepler thus eliminated the time-honored concept of circular orbits. The results of nine years of labor were published in 1609 in his *Astronomia Nova* (*New Astronomy*) in which Kepler presented his First and Second Laws. These laws may be stated very briefly as follows:

First Law: Every planet moves around the sun in an elliptical path, with the sun at one focal point of the ellipse.

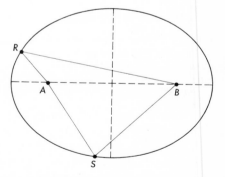

Fig. 1.10 An ellipse is a geometric figure for which the sum of the distances of a point on the curve to the focal points will equal the sum of the distances of any other point on the curve to the focal points. Thus, we find that *AS + SB* will equal *AR + RB*.

An ellipse may be defined as a geometric figure or curve for which the sum of the distances of a point on the curve to the focal points will equal the sums of the distances of any other point on the curve to the focal points (Fig. 1.10). While the planetary orbit is defined as an ellipse, the degree of eccentricity of these orbits is so small that if the figures were drawn to scale, the ellipse could not be readily distinguished from a circle just by casual observation.

Second Law: A line connecting the planet and the sun will sweep over equal areas in equal times as the planet moves in its orbit.

The path and speed of a planet are such that the planet will move from *K* to *L* in the same length of time that it takes the planet to go from *O* to *P*. The planet moves at a more rapid speed at *KL* and at a slower speed at *OP*. However, due to the distance from the sun, the area swept during like periods of time by the imaginary line from the sun to the planet will always be equal (Fig. 1.11).

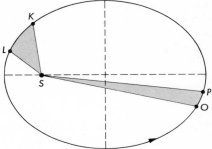

Fig. 1.11   An imaginary line from the planet to the sun will sweep over equal areas in an equal period of time. Therefore the area of *KLS* is equal to the area of *OPS*.

Having determined the nature of the orbit and the speed of motion traveled by the planets, Kepler next set out to discover whether a relationship existed between a planet's distance from the sun and its period of revolution. Kepler had no real plan for attacking this task. He felt that such a relationship existed and to find it he resorted to a trial-and-error procedure.

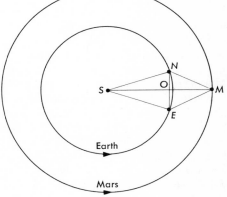

Fig. 1.12   Kepler's method of determining the distances from the sun to Mars in astronomical units.

First it was necessary for Kepler to calculate the distance of the various planets from the sun. This he accomplished in a rather ingenious way by using the distance from the earth to the sun as the unit of measurement and relating other planetary distances to this unit. This unit of distance from the earth to the sun has become known as an *astronomical unit* (AU). Using Mars to illustrate Kepler's method, we must assume that Mars is at *M* when the earth is at *N* (Fig. 1.12). Mars takes 687 days to return to point *M*, during which time the earth has made almost two passages around the sun, arriving at point *E*. The difference between one Martian year of 687 days and two earth years or 730½ days is 43½ days which is the length of time represented by the arc *NE*.

It is, therefore, possible to calculate the angle *NSE*, since it is equal to the arc *NE*. At the same time, *NS* is equal to *ES*, since these are the radii of the earth's orbit and are equal to 1 AU. Thus there exists an isosceles triangle for which two sides and an angle are known, making it possible to solve for the base *NE*, the two base angles *SNE* and *SEN*, and the line *OS*. It is also possible to solve for the triangle *NME*, since side *NE* is known as well as *MNS* and the angle *MES*. Similarly the angle *MNE* is the difference between the angles *MNS* and *ENS*. With this information we can find *OM* and by combining it with *OS*, compute the distance from Mars to the sun on a scale where the distance from the earth to the sun equals 1 AU.

It was from this type of data that Kepler finally achieved his goal of relating time and distance with respect to planetary motion. This relationship became his Third Law of Motion, published in his *De Harmonice Mundi* (*Harmony of the World*) in 1619. Quite simply this law states:

Third Law: The squares of the periods of any two planets are proportional to the cubes of their mean distances from the sun.

If *T* is taken as the time in years for one complete orbital revolution of a planet, and *R* is taken as the mean distance in astronomical units of that planet from the sun, then the relationship of any two planets would be

$$\frac{(T_1)^2}{(T_2)^2} = \frac{(R_1)^3}{(R_2)^3}$$

or

$$T^2 = kR^3,$$

where *k* equals 1 yr/1 AU when astronomical units are used.

While this law did not present any information that had not been previously known, it did present a relationship between the planets which had not been previously recognized. It was later to become extremely important, for it was from the Third Law of Motion that Newton derived his Universal Law of Gravitation.

Kepler's laws were a monumental contribution to the science of astronomy. He was able to show the physical structure of the Copernican system and satisfactorily explain planetary motion without the aid of artificial devices. At the same time, Kepler had accomplished another feat never before achieved, the formulation of a physical law in the language of mathematics. This was the first time in the history of science that a physical law had been sought and developed on the basis of previously accumulated data. So well did Kepler labor that, three hundred years after he presented them to the world, his laws are still valid with only minor modifications.

While Kepler toiled, another event took place that was to revolutionize the science of astronomy. This was the invention of the telescope, in 1608, by a Dutch spectacle maker, Hans Lippershey. Rumors about the instrument reached Galileo in Italy, and by 1609 he also had developed a telescope. The first celestial body on which Galileo turned his telescope was the moon. He found that the moon was not smooth as had always been thought but rather mountainous, with many craters and dark areas which he thought to be seas.

Galileo Galilei (1564–1642) was born in Pisa almost at the time of Michelangelo's death. He was educated at the University of Pisa, first in medicine and later in mathematics, physics, and astronomy. At the time that he developed his telescope, he was a professor of mathematics at the University of Padua and an excellent innovator in the art of introducing students to new concepts. It was Galileo who conceived of the idea of temperature and the thermometer, and he was the first to show that air had weight. Galileo, like Kepler, was a confirmed Copernican. With the development of the telescope and the observations that could be made with it, Galileo was able to contribute to the support of the heliocentric theory.

Galileo found that the moon had earthlike qualities and he was able to compute the heights of mountains on the moon, showing them to be as high as those on earth. He introduced the idea of *earthshine* which, through his telescope, he found to be a secondary illumination of the moon's dark surface. He was able to show geometrically that this light resulted from reflected sunlight from the earth. Galileo found that the stars were not magnified by his instrument but that numerous additional stars became visible. More than fifty stars were visible to Galileo in the Pleiades (Seven Sisters) where six or seven had previously been seen with the naked eye. The fact that the stars were not magnified in the same manner as the moon, he reasoned, must be due to the enormous distances of the stars from the earth. He was able to resolve the centuries-old problem of the nature of the Milky Way when he found it, too, to be made up of a multitude of stars.

The planets appeared as small round disks and shone with a reflected light from the sun. He discovered that Venus not only went through a cycle of phase changes but also underwent a change in size. This was further proof to Galileo that Venus orbited the sun. Venus was relatively large when it was between the earth and the sun and showed only a thin crescent. When this occurred, the sun would be shining on the side opposite to that of the earth, and the night-time side of Venus would be facing the earth. When Venus was seen as a complete disk, that planet would be opposite the sun from the earth and would appear to be quite small.

Additional proof to support Galileo's belief in the Copernican system was found when he viewed Jupiter. On January 7, 1610, ". . . the planet Jupiter presented itself to my view . . ." Galileo noticed what he thought were three small but bright stars associated with Jupiter in a straight line, two to the left and one to the right of the large planet. This alone did not particularly excite him, but on the following night he discovered all three stars on the right side of Jupiter. Galileo continued observing and was able to see an almost hourly change in position. On January 13, 1610, he discovered the fourth satellite which, along with the other three, was on a straight line with the planet's equator. Galileo concluded that these bodies were indeed satellites of Jupiter revolving around the planet as the moon revolves around the earth, and traveling with Jupiter in its orbit around the sun. Galileo felt that if these satellites revolved around Jupiter, then it should not be too difficult to believe that the planets revolved around the sun. This was thought by Galileo to be another argument in favor of the heliocentric system.

Other discoveries were to be made by Galileo. He viewed Saturn which, because of the inadequacies of his telescope, appeared as a disk with "ears." Galileo was unable to fathom this puzzle, and it was some time later and with the aid of better equipment, that the true nature of the rings of Saturn was revealed. Galileo also looked at the sun, and for his pains he was temporarily blinded and his eyesight permanently impaired. Learning from this, a Jesuit priest, Christopher Scheiner, viewed the sun first through clouds, then through a lens made of dark glass, and finally through a sooted piece of glass held between the sun and his telescope. He was the first to see sunspots on the sun's surface. Galileo later caught images of the sun on pieces of paper in a darkened room. In this manner he discovered that sunspots moved across the face of the sun, disappeared around one edge, and then reappeared around the other edge. From these observations, it was evident to Galileo that the sun rotated on its axis just as the earth did.

Galileo's discoveries were not immediately accepted by the scientific world. Some of his colleagues even refused to look through the telescope to verify what he had seen. The greatest resistance Galileo experienced came from the academic community at the universities. Tradition was most difficult to overcome, particularly since it involved the Aristotelian concepts held to be correct for almost 2000 years. The leaders of the Catholic Church, often credited with the sole responsibility of muzzling Galileo, actually had much praise for him. Jesuit astronomers found a great deal of value in his work although they still used the Copernican theory as a convenient means of making mathematical computations on planetary movements. It was from the lower echelons of the Church that Galileo was brought to the attention of the Inquisition. He defended himself well and enlisted his many influential friends in the aid of his cause. The result was that he received no more than a warning delivered to him through his friend Cardinal Bellarmine, in 1615. This warning consisted of enjoining Galileo from teaching that the sun was the center of the planetary system. At this time, Copernicus' book was also officially blacklisted. Thus the teaching of the heliocentric theory was banned by the Catholic as well as by the Protestant and Jewish hierarchies.

Galileo continued his studies but refrained from teaching or writing on this forbidden subject. In 1623 his friend, Cardinal Barberini, who had previously intervened on Galileo's behalf, was elected Pope. The new Pope favored Galileo and praised him highly, thus encouraging Galileo to write a defense of the heliocentric theory supported by his own findings. His book, *Dialogue on the Two Chief Systems of the World,* was brilliantly done and widely acclaimed even by high officials in the Catholic Church. However, the book, which came off the press in February, 1632, was confiscated in August, and Galileo was again called to face a special commission of the Inquisition.

His book was banned and Galileo was committed to permanent house arrest in his country home near Florence. Here, for the remaining days of his life, he devoted himself to his former professions, mathematics and engineering, and wrote *Dialogue Concerning Two New Sciences,* in which he developed the science of dynamics.

During the course of history there have been occasions when a need has arisen for some cohesive force to bring ideas or events to a climax. Such a force was the genius of Isaac Newton, born in 1642, the same year in which Galileo died. Newton was able to combine the various ideas of Copernicus, Kepler, and Galileo into a cohesive whole and explain the behavior of the planets and the forces that influenced them.

Newton, born near Grantham in Lincolnshire, though frail as a boy, took an early interest in science and the laws of physics. He describes one of his earliest experiments as taking place in the midst of a thunderstorm during which he measured the force of the wind by determining the length of his stride when running into and with the wind. He describes this as having taken place ". . . the year Cromwell died . . ." and ever after was to remember investigations he had made in relation to some historical event.

Newton entered Cambridge in 1661 at the age of 19 to study mathematics. He was a brilliant student and by the age of 24 had made several valuable contributions to science by developing the binomial theorem, differential calculus, and enunciating the theory of colors. So unusual was Newton's ability that the professor under whom Newton had worked for his doctorate retired so that Newton could replace him.

One of Newton's first major contributions was the construction of a telescope which made use of mirrors instead of lenses to gather and focus light. Newton had been disturbed by the distortion of the image due to the colored fringes of the lenses. The use of mirrors eliminated this problem. He also found that passing sunlight through a prism divided the white light into a number of bands of colored light, the spectrum. Further experimentation showed that these colors were primary colors and were the component parts of white light.

Newton's greatest triumph is generally recognized by everyone as his Universal Law of Gravitation. As frequently happens in the scientific world, Newton worked on this problem simultaneously with, but independent of, two other scientists. Robert Hooke, also an Englishman, demonstrated that, following Galileo's law of Inertia, the planets would move in a straight line, but that the sun attracted them and caused the planets to orbit the sun. Giovanni Borelli of Italy also recognized the existence of two forces, one causing the body to move in a straight line and another force at right angles to the direction of motion.

At the age of 24, Newton set himself the task of defining these forces in precise mathematical terms. Newton and his contemporaries did not originate this concept of a force between celestial bodies, for Kepler often spoke of the influence of the force of the sun on the other planets. It was known that the moon had an approximately circular orbit with a radius 60 times the radius of the earth and a period of revolution slightly over 27 days. Galileo had established the fact that matter falls to the earth's surface with an acceleration of 32 feet per second per second. In the first second an object such as an apple, starting at rest, would fall a distance of 16 feet. Following Galileo's line of thought, Newton concluded that the moon moving around the earth was influenced by a similar force and that this force must originate in the earth.

Newton made use of an hypothesis, proposed several years before his birth by an unknown scientist, that the force of attraction of one body for another was inversely proportional to the square of the distance between them. Later, Newton was able to show that this was, in fact, implied in Kepler's Third Law. This meant that if the moon were 60 earth radii from the earth, the force acting on the moon was $\frac{1}{60^2}$ or $\frac{1}{3600}$ the force acting on the apple. Newton knew that the apple fell 16 feet in the first second, so he deduced that the moon should "fall" toward the earth $\frac{1}{3600}$ of this distance in an equal amount of time or a distance of 0.0044 feet. Knowing the speed of the moon in orbit and the length of the orbit, Newton was able to calculate the actual fall and found it to be about $\frac{1}{6}$ smaller than it should have been theoretically and, being of a precise nature, he was discouraged by the results. Sixteen years later new calculations were made by the French to show that the diameter of the earth was about $\frac{1}{6}$ larger than had previously been thought. Using this new figure, Newton recalculated and found that the result was almost exact.

Newton extended his work to prove that all bodies exhibited a force of gravity whereby they mutually attracted each other, and that the force was proportional to the product of the mass of the two bodies and inversely proportional to the square of the distance between them.

$$\text{Force of gravity} = \frac{\text{Product of the masses of two objects}}{\text{Square of the distance between them}}.$$

The law of gravity has proved extremely useful in astronomy, since it can be used to determine the mass of the other planets, distant stars, and remote nebulas. The cause of gravity and its innate properties are unknown; only the force exerted is measurable. In addition to showing that the force of gravity exerted by the earth kept the moon in its orbit, Newton demonstrated that the sun accounted for the orbital motions of the various planets. Newton also explained the precession of the earth as being due to the fact that the sun's gravitational force does not pass through the exact center of the earth. This occurs because the earth is not a perfect sphere but, rather, slightly flattened at its poles. He was also able to show that the tidal action of the oceans was the result of the gravitational attractive forces of the moon and the sun. All these discoveries were to be published in the *Mathematical Principles of Natural Philosophy* or *Principia* in 1686 by the Royal Society. Due to a lack of funds, however, the society was unable to publish the work and Edmund Halley, for whom the comet was later to be named, published it at his own expense.

Newton's work has remained valid through the years so that even in the twentieth century, the law has not been "repealed." What was true in 1686 is, even with all the precise measuring equipment, "almost true" in the present. The law of gravity has been useful in predicting the presence of planets, as yet unseen, on the basis of irregularities in the orbits of visible planets, and the presence of invisible stars closely associated with the bright visible ones. However, to account for the slight discrepancies that appeared as a result of more precise measurements, a new theory was needed. This was supplied by Albert Einstein in the twentieth century.

When Newton developed his law of gravity he was, like others in his age, still influenced by the Aristotelian concept of an absolute immutable universe giving a fixed standard of reference for measuring the position of any object in space. Certain movements have since been noted which can not be accounted for by Newtonian physics. Among these is the rotation of Mercury's orbital ellipse which advances through 43 seconds of arc every 100 years. Observations of this type have become available only because of increased precision in measurement. This increase in precision has also made it possible to show that the universe is not standing still but that every visible object, regardless of how remote, is in motion.

When the fixed frame of reference disappeared, it became necessary to seek a new foundation from which to make observations. Einstein maintained that no such base or foundation existed. The measurements of mass, length, and time were dependent on the state of motion of the objects to be measured. The faster an object moved, the larger became its mass. This has been confirmed in numerous experiments employing electron accelerators where electrons in powerful magnetic fields were speeded up almost to the speed of light. Under these conditions, their mass is enormously increased. To illustrate his idea of relative motion and position in space, Einstein discussed the motion of a pebble dropped from the window of a moving railroad car. He pointed out that to the person riding in the car and dropping the pebble, the pebble appeared to fall to the ground in a straight line. To an observer outside the train watching this event, the pebble appeared to fall in a parabolic curve because of the motion imparted to it by the train. Einstein then asked, which is the true motion? Actually, he explained, there is no absolute point from which this motion can be described. It is necessary, therefore, to define the frame of reference *relative* to which the motion is observed.

It would not be accurate to say that Einstein's theories explain all the phenomena relating to mass, motion, and time. His theories are truer than Newton's only to the extent that they define the laws of nature more closely. Newton's laws, in turn, were a refinement of Kepler's work. This did not mean that Kepler was wrong, but that Newton was able to explain events in nature more precisely because of better measurements. No doubt in due time a reexamination of Einstein's theories will be necessary in the light of discoveries yet to be made.

1.5 THE SCIENTIFIC METHOD

Two general approaches to solving the secrets of nature are recognized, *inductive* and *deductive reasoning*. The first of these proceeds from the particular items of observation or experimentation to the more general conclusions that can be drawn from these observations. Aristotle was prone to make observations from which he developed broad concepts to explain the laws of nature. While the inductive method is the foundation of modern experimental science, Aristotle erred because he conducted too few experiments as a basis for his theories. Following the same procedure Kepler, using the data acquired from Brahe, was able to develop a theory so broad in its application that it took on the stature of a scientific law.

Copernicus, on the other hand, made use of the deductive form of reasoning in evolving his heliocentric theory. The deductive method starts with the expression of an hypothesis or broad generalization and then, by testing, determines the truth of this hypothesis. For example, Copernicus expressed the hypothesis that the planets orbited the sun rather than vice versa as had been universally held. He then calculated the positions of these planets at various times during the year and compared these data with the actual observed positions. Finding good agreement between the calculated and the observed positions he was able to establish the validity of his original hypothesis, whereupon it could be considered a theory. It can readily be seen that to develop a theory by this method requires a considerable amount of intuitive insight into the workings of nature.

From the foregoing brief account of the development of astronomy, it is possible to see how science progresses. Knowledge is gained step by step, each scientist benefiting from the work of those who preceded him. Newton best expressed this when he remarked on his achievements by saying that if he had seen further than others it was by standing upon the shoulders of giants.

Each advance has been demonstrated to be an improvement on what existed before. Science has not proved the new theories to be correct, but only that they are more adequate in describing the laws of nature than the theories they replace. Science, through the process of the scientific method, approaches the truth. It is not possible to say whether science will ever fully achieve it.

1.6 SUMMARY

Astronomy as practiced by ancient civilizations was closely associated with mythology. Some work of scientific value was done, but was usually performed for religious reasons. Not until the Greeks achieved a high degree of culture did astronomy take on a truly scientific significance. Two schools of thought prevailed with respect to the organization of the universe, but Aristotle's influence led to the dominance of the geocentric theory. This concept envisioned an earth-centered universe with all celestial bodies moving around the earth in rigidly defined circular orbits.

It was not until the sixteenth century that Copernicus found that the motions of the planets and stars were better described on the basis of a heliocentric or sun-centered universe. Copernicus, however, still maintained the concept of uniform circular motion as originated by the Greeks. In the early part of the seventeenth century Johannes Kepler, using the data collected by Tycho Brahe, discovered that the true motion of the planets about the sun was in an elliptical orbit. Kepler's work of many years led to the formulation of his three laws of motion, a valuable contribution to the science of astronomy.

While Kepler was working on his laws of motion, Galileo developed his telescope and discovered the true nature of the moon and the four major satellites of Jupiter. Following the invention of the telescope new discoveries came at a rapid rate, adding to the ever-increasing store of knowledge.

Another giant of the seventeenth century was Isaac Newton. His Law of Universal Gravitation contributed greatly to understanding why every body in the universe maintained its relative position with respect to other bodies. In brief, his law stated that every body attracts any other body with a force proportional to the product of their masses and inversely proportional to the square of the distance between them. He also made slight improvements on Kepler's Laws of Motion to increase their accuracy.

In the nineteenth century, however, a slight discrepancy in the orbit of Mercury was discovered, which could not be accounted for even by Newton's Laws. It was left to Einstein in 1915 to further refine the theories explaining the movement of celestial bodies. In his General Theory of Relativity, discussing the nature of the curvature of space around large bodies, Einstein theorized that small celestial bodies revolved around large bodies by following this curvature. This was later proved to be fact, and it was shown how aberrations in Mercury's orbit which could not be accounted for by Newton's gravitational mathematics could be accounted for by relativistic mathematics.

Many advances have been made since this discovery in what was believed in the nineteenth century to be an exhausted science. Since Einstein's discoveries, new instrumentation and new techniques have rapidly advanced knowledge in astronomy. The advent of space exploration makes accuracy in the location of solar bodies imperative.

SUGGESTED READINGS

ANTHONY, H. D., *Sir Isaac Newton*. New York: Collier Books, 1960.

CASPAR, M., *Kepler 1571–1630*. New York: Collier Books, 1959.

HOLTON G., and D. H. D. ROLLER, *Foundations of Modern Physical Science*. Reading, Mass.: Addison-Wesley, 1958.

KUHN, T. S., *The Copernican Revolution*. New York: Random House, 1959.

MASON, S. F., *A History of Science*. New York: Collier Books, 1962.

TAYLOR, F. S., *Galileo and the Freedom of Thought*. London: Watt and Co., 1938.

YOUNG, L. B., ed., *Exploring the Universe*. New York: McGraw-Hill, 1963.

CHAPTER 2

THE ASTRONOMER'S TOOLS

How is it possible to study the nature of objects so vastly distant from the earth? The answer lies in the manner in which light is gathered, focused, and analyzed. The human eye is capable of performing the first two of these functions while the brain analyzes the light impulse received by the eye. Does the eye "see" objects millions of miles away? Actually, it does not. The light travels to the eye, stimulates the nerve endings on the retina, and a nerve impulse to the brain is interpreted as the sensation of vision. The idea that light was a property of its point of origin rather than of the eye of the observer was first realized in the eleventh century, but it was not until the seventeenth century that light was recognized as a form of energy.

2.1 THE NATURE OF LIGHT

The ancient Greeks first discussed the nature of light. Some of them believed that light consisted of tiny particles emitted by the light source. Aristotle rejected this concept and suggested that light resulted from some activity occurring between the light source and the eye.

In 1678 Christian Huygens, a Dutch mathematician, brought forth the idea that light traveled in waves in the same manner as waves on water. Huygens compared the propagation of light with that of sound, wherein the air is set to vibrating and the vibration is transmitted from one molecule of air to the next until the vibrations reach the ear. He felt that light was an oscillation of ether, a substance then thought to fill space, and that this oscillation was detected by the eye.

Newton had a different concept of light because he did not believe in the existence of ether. He maintained that light waves were nonexistent because there was no ether to transmit them, and he reverted to the Greek idea that light consisted of corpuscles or tiny particles passing through empty space. Newton also contended that when light entered a denser medium such as glass or water, the speed of the particle increased as a result of a mutual gravitational force between the particle and the medium it was entering. The wave theory, on the other hand, required that when light entered a denser medium its velocity decreases. Newton, however, did not completely discard the wave theory. He had done considerable work with color and suggested that waves set up by the corpuscle moving through a particular medium resulted in the development of color. The color sensation, he felt, depended on the frequency of the waves or vibrations set up by the passage of the corpuscle through the medium, much the same as sound depended on different vibrations of air. Newton's corpuscular theory enjoyed popularity for some time, not because it was more provable than the wave theory, but because of Newton's tremendous reputation.

In the 1850's a Frenchman, Jean Foucault, was able to demonstrate that the velocity of light did decrease as it entered a denser medium, thereby deciding the issue in favor

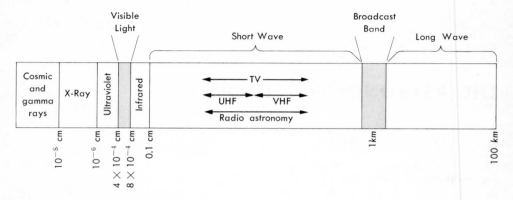

Fig. 2.1   Range of electromagnetic radiation.

of the wave theory. It did not prove that the wave theory was correct, but it did prove that the corpuscular theory was based on an erroneous assumption.

Continued study on the nature of light gradually revealed phenomena which again led to the corpuscular theory. Evidence became available which suggested that light was a stream of particles of definite size and measurable energy and that the light particles moved in a manner indicating wave motion. The exact nature of light is still not completely resolved. However, certain physical properties of light are measurable and are useful in solving the mysteries of distant objects in space.

Usually, when speaking of light, one includes only the visible portion of the entire electromagnetic wave phemonemon. Visible light makes up a relatively small segment of electromagnetic activity, which ranges from cosmic rays with the extremely short wavelength of 10^{-11} cm to the very long radio waves 100 km in length, as illustrated in Fig. 2.1.

The shortest of the electromagnetic waves are the cosmic rays coming from outer space. Next in length are gamma rays which have their source in radioactive materials. Gamma rays are useful in treating certain malignancies and in radioactive tracer work. Next longest are the X-rays used for photographing bone structure in the human body and, in industry, for checking the internal stresses of materials. Ultraviolet light, still invisible to the naked eye, is of longer wavelength than X-rays and shorter than visible light. The sun is a primary source of ultraviolet light which is responsible for sunburn. Fortunately, most of the sun's ultraviolet light is absorbed by water vapor in the atmosphere, for this form of radiation in large doses is harmful to humans. Visible light ranges from violet to red, increasing in wavelength until the longer infrared waves are reached which are again invisible. Infrared waves are a source of heat, and this property is used, for example, to detect industrial complexes by means of high altitude photographic equipment that is sensitive to infrared waves. Beyond the infrared are the electrical and radio waves useful in radio, television, and radio astronomy. These wavelengths range up to several kilometers in length. The lines between the various types of waves shown in Fig. 2.1 are not clear-cut and overlap slightly. One property the waves all have in common is that the energy is propagated at the velocity of light or about 186,000 miles per second.

2.2   TELESCOPES

Almost all that is known of distant objects in the sky has been determined from the light reflected or emanating from them. Without the aid of instruments, ancient astronomers could only define motion and position of celestial bodies. The invention of the telescope, 350 years ago, was a great boost in that it permitted observation of greater detail on the bodies in the solar system. It also made it possible to view many smaller bodies that could not be seen with the naked eye, and to measure planetary motion more accurately. While there are two fundamentally different types of telescopes, they serve the same primary purpose of gathering and focusing light, thereby permitting the distinction between two points that are close together in the sky and magnifying the object to make it appear closer to the viewer.

Refracting Telescopes.   The telescope first used by Galileo utilized lenses through which the light was bent or refracted to a focus. Refraction occurs when light passes from a less dense medium such as air, to a denser one such as glass or water. The degree of refraction from any transparent material can be measured and is always the same for that substance under similar circumstances. A ray of light entering a lens strikes the lens at point P (Fig. 2.2). When entering a dense medium, in this case the glass, the ray is bent toward the normal N_1. The normal N_1 is a line perpendicular to a tangent T_1 to the point of entry at P. Thus the angle of incidence, i_1, is larger than the angle of refraction, r_1. When leaving a dense medium for the air the light ray is bent away from the normal. In this instance the angle of incidence, i_2, is smaller than the angle of refraction, r_2. Light from a single distant source (a planet or star) would presumably enter the objective lens (Fig. 2.3) as parallel rays which would be brought to a single focus at F. The distance between the center of the lens and F is the focal length. Light from several sources would enter the lens from slightly different angles and therefore would not focus at the same point but would focus on the same plane (Fig. 2.3).

If portions of the sky are to be photographed, the photographic plate is positioned so that the active surface of the plate will fall on the focal plane. This arrangement, while suitable for photographing distant objects, is not used for visual observation.

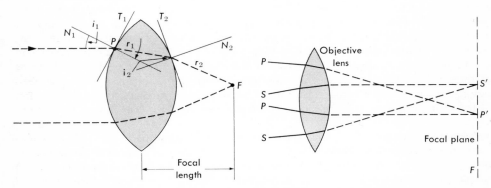

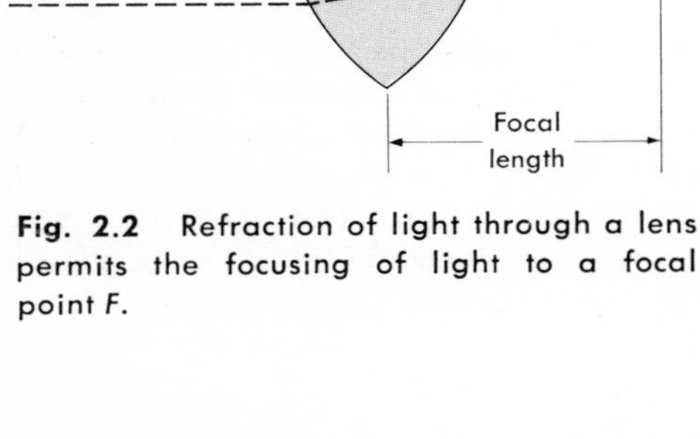

Fig. 2.2   Refraction of light through a lens permits the focusing of light to a focal point F.

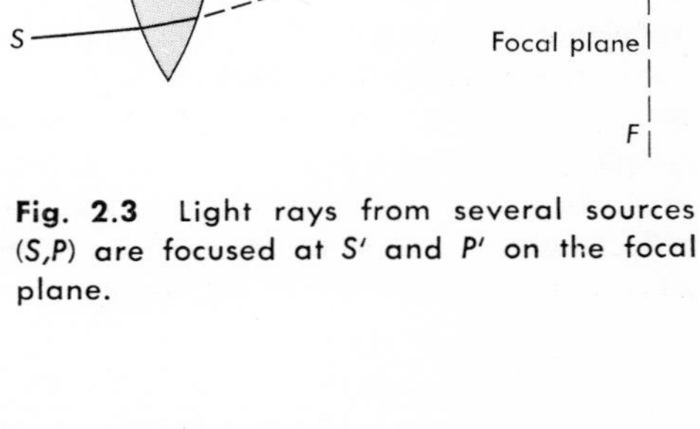

Fig. 2.3   Light rays from several sources (S,P) are focused at S' and P' on the focal plane.

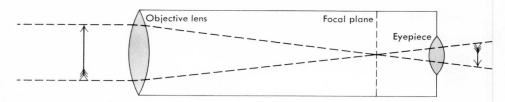

Fig. 2.4   A simple refracting telescope.

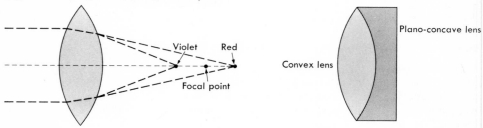

Fig. 2.5   Chromatic aberration of a lens.   **Fig. 2.6   An achromatic lens.**

For visual observation, the light from the focal plane must be bent again so that the rays enter the eye in a parallel manner. This is accomplished by an eyepiece which is a lens similar to the objective lens but small enough to accommodate the human eye. The image as received on the retina of the eye, after passing through the eyepiece, would be inverted (Fig. 2.4).

One of the serious problems with a refracting telescope is that of chromatic aberration, which is a dispersion of light of differing wavelengths (color) by the lens. The refraction of a ray of white light is actually the composite or average refraction of all visible light. Violet light is bent the most by a lens and, therefore, is focused closer to the objective lens than is red light, which is bent the least (Fig. 2.5). This results in a rainbow-colored fringe around the image of each object, thus blurring the view through a refracting telescope. The effect of this form of aberration is reduced by using a compound lens of two or more components. In 1758 John Dollond, an English optician, developed an achromatic lens of two parts, one a double convex lens of crown glass and the other a plano-concave lens of flint glass (Fig. 2.6). With such a lens, two colors can be brought to a single focus; a lens of three components will permit the focusing of three colors. While this does not completely solve the problem of chromatic aberration, it reduces it to a manageable form. If care is taken in choosing the wavelengths of light for corrections that are most important in viewing, the lens is very satisfactory.

Reflecting Telescopes. The second fundamental type of telescope is the reflecting telescope developed by Isaac Newton to overcome the problem of chromatic aberration. In place of the objective lens, a mirror is used to accomplish focusing of the light rays. A simple form of reflecting telescope is shown in Fig. 2.7(a). The concave mirror is placed at the base of the telescope and is formed in the shape of a paraboloid. This shape will reflect light to the prime focus (F) at which point a photographic plate can be placed to record the image. The light coming to the mirror is partially obscured by the photo-

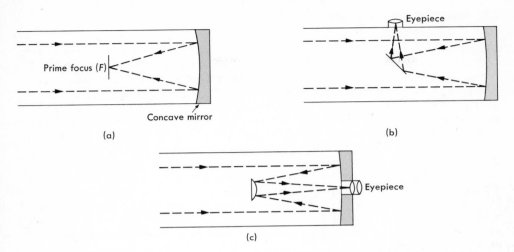

Fig. 2.7 Types of optical systems used in reflecting telescopes: (a) prime focus; (b) Newtonian focus; (c) Cassegrainian focus.

graphic equipment or by a secondary mirror which is used to reflect the light to an eyepiece. The partial loss of the light entering the telescope cannot be avoided but is kept to a minimum, usually less than 10%.

The secondary mirror is a flat mirror which simply diverts the light from the main parabolic mirror to the eyepiece located outside the telescope tube (Fig. 2.7b). The secondary mirror does not affect the image in any way, but only redirects it to a more convenient viewing or photographing location. This type of telescope is known as the *Newtonian system.* The *Cassegrainian system* (Fig. 2.7c) is an alternative form using a convex secondary mirror to direct the image through an opening in the main mirror. A convex secondary mirror is used to focus the light beyond the back of the main mirror since a flat mirror would focus the light inside the telescope tube. The effect of such a system is to increase the focal length of the telescope.

Chromatic aberration is not a problem in reflecting telescopes because the light does not pass through the glass, but, instead, is reflected from an aluminized or silvered surface. Reflecting telescopes form excellent images close to the center of the mirror, but toward the edge a form of aberration called *coma* develops. Toward the edge of pictures taken with a reflecting telescope stars appear to have tails pointing toward the perimeter of the field. This effect becomes more pronounced as the edge of the field is approached. Another problem with reflecting telescopes is that the main concave mirror does not reflect uniformly so that different concentric zones of the mirror will focus the image at different positions. This *spherical aberration,* as it is known, is of a uniform nature and may be corrected by using a correcting plate. The correcting plate is a lens that bends light just enough to compensate for this type of aberration. This combining of lens and mirror into a most satisfactory telescope was accomplished by Bernard Schmidt in 1931. The *Schmidt telescope* was immediately found to be most useful for wide-angle photographic work, but because a curved surface is required to receive the corrected image, this telescope is not suitable for visual observation.

2.3 TELESCOPE PERFORMANCE

One of the first questions asked about a telescope pertains to its magnifying power. Early telescopes were of relatively low power; Galileo's best instrument magnified 33 times. To overcome the problem of chromatic aberration and to increase magnification, telescopes in the seventeenth century were made with extremely long focal lengths requiring telescopes up to 150 feet long. These were called *air* telescopes because the instrument was not enclosed in a tube to shield the image from unnecessary light. The development of an achromatic lens by Dollond lent some impetus to the development of larger refracting telescopes. The largest refracting telescope built by the middle of the nineteenth century, however, had an aperture (diameter of the objective lens) of only 9 inches. At present the largest refracting telescope in the world is located at the Yerkes observatory in Williams Bay, Wisconsin. This instrument is equipped with a 40-inch objective lens which may well be the largest practical size for this type of telescope. The great weight of the lens is supported only at its rim and the slightest distortion of the glass as a result of bending would more than offset the advantage gained by increasing its size.

The problem of support is not inherent in the reflecting telescope. However, this was not a factor in the development of the reflector by Newton in about 1670. He utilized a mirror in place of a lens to overcome the chromatic aberration. While this problem was solved, some difficulty was experienced in grinding a proper surface which would reflect light to a common focal plane. Despite this difficulty, many fine instruments were built, particularly by Herschel, who by the end of the eighteenth century had built a 48-inch reflector. The mirror itself was made of metal, a bronze alloy, which reflected about 60% of the light when it was polished. The disadvantage of such a mirror was that it became tarnished and easily corroded, enough so that it no longer reflected light accurately unless it was resurfaced.

The largest metal mirror was built by William Parsons of Ireland, third Earl of Rosse, in 1845. The 72-inch disk weighed 4 tons and took 17 years to build. The tube was 45 feet long and looked like a leaning industrial smokestack. This Leviathan, as it was called, was so sensitive to wind movement that it had to be enclosed on two sides to shield it.

By the twentieth century, glass was being used for mirrors, and George Hale, developer of the 40-inch Yerkes telescope, designed the 60-inch and the 100-inch reflectors for Mount Wilson and the 200-inch Mount Palomar telescope. The last of these great telescopes was put into use in 1948, but Hale did not live to see it. This giant telescope was not designed for celestial hunts. Only known objects of interest are photographed with it because only a very small segment of the sky can be covered at one time. It has been suggested that 5000 years would be required to make a complete map of the sky with this instrument.

The magnifying power of any of these instruments is the amount by which an object appears larger than it does to the naked eye. By the same token, magnification may be expressed as the amount by which an object's apparent distance is reduced. Magnification is obtained only through the use of an objective lens eyepiece combination and is obtained by the relationship of their respective focal lengths expressed as

$$M = \frac{F}{f},$$

where F is the focal length of the objective lens and f is the focal length of the eyepiece. Thus if F is equal to 25 inches and f is equal to ½ inch, $M = 25/(½) = 50$ diameters. The moon viewed through such an instrument would appear 50 times larger in diameter than when viewed with the naked eye or it would appear as though it were at ¹⁄₅₀th its real distance from the earth.

Fig. 2.8 An increase in magnification decreases the actual field of view. With low magnification (a) the field of view is large showing the entire tree. When magnification is increased, (b) the field of view is reduced so that only a portion of the tree is visible.

(a)   (b)

Magnification cannot be increased indefinitely, since there are some limitations to the use of high magnification. One of these is the decrease in the size of the field with increased magnification (see Fig. 2.8). As previously mentioned, the 200-inch Hale telescope, while magnifying many diameters, views only a small segment of the sky. Greater magnification would further reduce this field. The *field of view* as seen through a telescope can be determined from the apparent field of view of the eyepiece in degrees (usually supplied by the manufacturer) and the telescope's magnification:

$$\text{Field of view} = \frac{\text{Apparent field of eyepiece}}{\text{Magnification}}.$$

A telescope with an eyepiece having a field of view of 25° and magnifying 50 diameters has an actual field of view of ½°. This is just large enough to permit a view of the entire moon through the telescope since the moon has an angular diameter of about ½°.

Increased magnification also results in increased "twinkling" of the stars. This phenomenon is produced by movement of the earth's atmosphere. This atmospheric movement causes the light from the star to appear to change in position and brightness. While not a serious problem with small telescopes it sometimes prohibits the use of a large telescope on otherwise clear nights.

Practical limits of magnification have been established, based on the clarity of image, the resolving power, and the obtainable field of view. Maximum magnification is limited to about 50 times the diameter of the objective lens, which means that the practical upper limit of magnification for the 200-inch telescope is about 10,000 diameters. The minimum practical magnification has been determined to be about four times the diameter of the objective lens.

Magnification is not the only criterion by which a telescope's performance is measured. The light-gathering power is also considered and again is measured against the ability of the naked eye. The amount of light gathered by an optical device, whether it be a telescope objective lens, mirror, or the pupil of the eye, is dependent on the area of the aperture. Comparing the eye with a telescope or one telescope with another, we find that the light-gathering power is proportional to the square of the diameter of the apertures. This relationship may be expressed as

$$\text{Light-gathering ability} = \frac{(\text{Diameter of telescope objective})^2}{(\text{Diameter of eye pupil})^2}.$$

For example, if the diameter of the aperture through which light enters the eye is ¼ inch and a telescope has a 6-inch mirror then the telescope has a light-gathering ability of 576 times that of the eye. The relationship of the light-gathering power of two telescopes may be determined in the same manner. The 200-inch telescope on Mount Palomar has four times the light-gathering power of the 100-inch telescope on Mount Wilson. This means that the 200-inch telescope is capable of gathering light from stars that are four times fainter than those from which light can be gathered by the 100-inch telescope.

The combination of magnification and light-gathering power are factors which must be considered when surface areas of objects in the solar system are viewed. Two telescopes with the same apertures will gather the same amount of light. If one telescope has a magnification twice that of the other, it will form an image which is twice as large in diameter or has four times the area. Therefore each unit of area from the more highly magnified surface will be only one-fourth as bright. These relationships are of great importance when objects are being photographed.

The clarity with which objects that are distant but close together can be distinguished is a function of the resolving power of an optical instrument. The eye is capable of resolving the print on an eye-testing chart at a standard distance of 20 feet. At a greater distance, these letters can no longer be distinguished. Experiments have shown that the eye cannot separate two objects which are less than 6 minutes (0.1°) of arc apart. Two lights which appear as separate entities at a distance of 10 feet appear as one light at 1000 feet. The same is true of distant stars. Many stars which appear as one to the unaided eye are, in reality, two or more stars in a group. For example Mizor, the second star in the handle of the Big Dipper, appears as one star to the eye, but even a small telescope will resolve it into two stars of a double-star system.

Light waves, when being focused by the objective lens or by the mirror, interfere with each other and are diffracted. This diffraction makes the star appear surrounded by several diffraction rings and produces a slightly hazy image instead of one clear point. If the diffraction rings of two close stars overlap, the stars are not resolved and appear as one star. Increased magnification does not help in this case, since the resolving power of a telescope is dependent on the size of the aperture and the wavelength of light. The ability of a telescope to resolve distant stars in seconds of arc may be determined by a simple formula called *Dawes rule:*

$$L = \frac{4.56}{a} \text{ seconds of arc.}$$

This formula gives the theoretical limit of resolution L of a telescope, where a is the diameter of the aperture. This means that a 10-inch telescope will resolve the components of any multiple star systems that are at least 0.456 second of arc apart.

2.4   AUXILIARY ATTACHMENTS

Stars appear as pinpoints of light in the telescope even with high magnification. Magnification alone is not the source of much of the information that has been gathered about the stars. One of the most useful tools used in association with the telescope is the *spectroscope*. It is so important to astronomy that spectroscopy will be discussed under a separate heading.

Although telescopes have become larger and magnification has become greater, the eye of the observer has not improved to match this technological advance. One piece of equipment which has been found as an excellent substitute for the eye is the camera. Most "observational" work with telescopes is at present photographic, since a photograph presents a number of distinct advantages over visual observation. It provides a permanent record useful in making a comparison of relative displacement of distant stars over a long period of time, and it permits study of the photographs at the convenience of the astronomer. Because of the accumulative effect of light energy on the sensitive surface of the photographic plate, the use of long-time exposures make it possible to resolve many faint and distant objects that the eye is unable to see. This technique has greatly increased the performance of the available telescopes and is responsible for much of the knowledge presently available in astronomy. Magnification of a photograph makes possible even more detailed studies of distant star groups. Even within the solar system, photography has been useful in the discovery of Pluto and many of the asteroids.

The temperature of many celestial bodies has been determined by means of a very sensitive thermocouple. A thermocouple consists of two wires of different composition joined together. When the point of attachment is subjected to heat, a measurable current will flow. A thermocouple placed at the focal point of a telescope can, in this manner, detect the heat radiation emanating from a celestial body, and the current flow will be a measure of the radiation.

The amount of light received from a star can be measured by means of the photoelectric cell. This device has been useful in determining distances to faint stars or star groups. The brightness of the light radiating from these stars can be compared with that from similar stars, the distance to which is known.

Another device similar in principle to the photoelectric cell is the image tube. The photoelectric cell is limited to measuring and recording the light of a single star while the image tube is capable of amplifying and recording the light of all the stars on a telescope's focal plane. Photographing this image is much more efficient than photographing the images at the focal plane directly. In this way the light-gathering power of a 10-inch telescope may become comparable to that of the 100-inch telescope.

2.5 SPECTROSCOPY

Newton's discovery that white light is a composite of several different colors had a far-reaching effect that even he could not foresee. In his work he permitted a beam of light (coming through a hole in the shade of his room) to pass through a prism and onto the wall of his room (Fig. 2.9). He was amazed at the colors produced and found by testing that neither the thickness of glass, the size of the opening in his shade, nor the position of the prism would alter the display of colors. He passed the colored rays

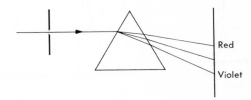

Fig. 2.9 Newton permitted light from a hole in his window blind to pass through a prism and onto the opposite wall.

Fig. 2.10 Newton's experiment with reversed prisms showed that the colors of
the spectrum, resulting from passage of
light through one prism, were recombined
into white light when passing through a
second reversed prism.

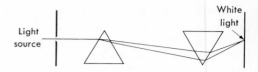

through a second prism turned in a reversed position and found that the colors were
recombined to form white light (Fig. 2.10). By permitting only one color to pass
through a second prism, he found that no change occurred, indicating that each color
was essentially a *pure* one (Fig. 2.11). By further experimentation, Newton was able
to ascertain that each color was bent or refracted at a different angle as it passed through
the prism, with violet light refracting the greatest amount and red refracting the least.
This band of colors which Newton named the *spectrum* was to be an extremely important tool for the astronomer.

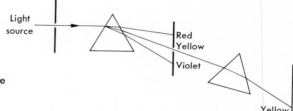

Fig. 2.11 Colors are shown to be
monochromatic.

In 1802 William Wollaston, an English scientist, discovered several dark lines in the
sun's spectrum. These lines were irregularly spaced; Wollaston, unable to fathom their
meaning, ignored them. Working with improved equipment, Joseph von Fraunhofer,
in 1814, observed the same phenomenon in the solar spectrum and mapped these dark
lines (Fig. 2.12). He first considered them the division points between the different
colors, but because of the lines' irregular spacing he discarded this idea. He assigned
letters to the more prominent lines but actually counted hundreds of them. The letters
still identify the Fraunhofer lines and are useful in designating approximate positions
in the visible spectrum.

In the late 1820's, Fraunhofer also developed a diffraction grating which permitted
the formation of the spectrum without the use of a prism. The grating consisted of a
number of slits made side by side by a precision machine able to make 300 slits to the
millimeter. A unit of measure called the angstrom (after Anders Angstrom) is now
used and is equal to one 10-millionth of a millimeter or one 250-millionth of an inch.

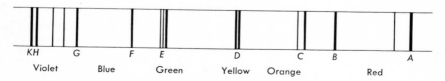

Fig. 2.12 A few of the Fraunhofer dark lines on the solar spectrum. [From Holton and
Roller, *Foundations of Physical Science*, 1958.]

Thus line *B* in the solar spectrum becomes 6378 angstroms (Å), and the wavelengths of light in the visible spectrum range from 7500 Å in the red end to about 4000 Å in the violet.

Gustav Kirchhoff of Germany was the first to show that certain elements yielded the same spectral lines, regardless of their source. In 1859 he showed that every element produces a "signature" on the spectrum which is different from that of all other elements. The number of lines varies tremendously: for example, iron has more than 1000 lines. With such a tool it became possible to examine the light received from celestial bodies and determine their composition. With this tool the science of astrophysics was born, and scientists were prepared to discover many new elements. However, they were doomed to disappointment; they soon found that distant stars were composed of the same elements found in the solar system.

The instrument used to make this analysis of light is called a *spectroscope* if visual examination is made or a *spectrograph* if a photographic record is made. The fundamental construction of these instruments is identical and varies only according to the manner in which the light is examined. As seen in Fig. 2.13, the spectrograph consists of a slit *A* through which light is admitted to the instrument from the light source. The light rays are made parallel by the collimator lens. These parallel rays enter the prism and are refracted into color light rays of a single wavelength. The lens at *D* brings the color light rays to a focus on the photographic plate at *E*. If the spectrum is to be viewed by eye, an eyepiece is used instead of a photographic plate.

A diffraction grating may be substituted for a prism in the spectroscope. The grating has the advantage of giving a larger spread to the spectrum, which permits more detailed examination. If the light to be analyzed is from a faint star or galaxy, then a prism is used since the prism concentrates the light and gives a brighter spectrum.

The spectroscope has been extremely useful not only in determining the composition of distant stars and galaxies but also, among other things, in measuring temperature, motion, and magnetic effect. The visible spectrum ranges in color from red to violet and, generally speaking, temperature is related to color. Temperatures which cause an object to be "red hot" are lower than those of an object that is "white hot." In the latter case, the emphasis of light energy has been shifted toward the violet end of the

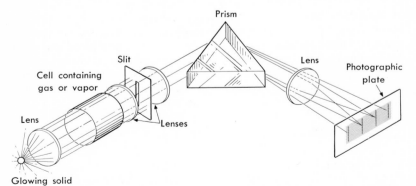

Fig. 2.13 Schematic diagram of a spectrograph. [From Holton and Roller, *Foundations of Physical Science,* 1958.]

spectrum. The sun has a temperature of about 10,400° F and has a yellow color. The energy of the visible light in the sun is highest in the yellow band of the spectrum; therefore this color is most pronounced. In 1895 Wilhelm Wien derived a formula for calculating temperatures of the sun and distant stars by spectroscopically determining the wavelength of light for which radiation was most intense. He found that there was a simple mathematical relationship between the wavelength of maximum radiation intensity, λ max (lambda maximum), expressed in angstroms, and absolute temperature, T, in degrees kelvin.* This relationship is expressed as

$$T = \frac{\text{constant}}{\lambda \text{ maximum}},$$

where the constant is equal to 2.898×10^7 Å-K.

Other stars, being hotter, will be white or blue because the blue wavelengths of light are more intense. By the same token, red stars are relatively cool, and the energy of the light is most pronounced in the red end of the spectrum. This has proved to be a very useful method for measuring temperatures of very distant stars.

Motion toward or away from an observer can also be detected spectroscopically. Use is made of the Doppler effect first described by Christian Doppler in 1842. His principle can be applied to both sound and light and is best illustrated in terms of the sound emitted by a locomotive whistle as it approaches or leaves an observer at high speed. On approaching the observer, the sound waves are in essence compressed, resulting in a high-pitched sound characteristic of sound waves with a short wavelength. Immediately on passing the observer, the sound drops to a low pitch characteristic of sound waves with a long wavelength.

The same effect is true of light moving toward or away from an observer. A distant galaxy, for example, moving away from an observer on the earth would have spectrum lines shifted toward the red end of the spectrum as compared to the spectrum of a stationary system. The wavelength of light from an object moving away from the earth is stretched out, thus taking on the characteristics of the longer wavelength of light found in the red end of the spectrum. This phenomenon is known as the *red-shift* and has been found useful in determining direction of radial motion of many distant objects. The light from a star or galaxy is concentrated by a telescope on the opening of a spectrograph and the star's spectrum is photographed. Immediately before and after the star's spectrum is photographed, a comparison photograph is made by the same spectrograph of the spectrum of some element (such as iron) just above and below the star's spectrum. The displacement of the iron lines in the star's spectrum compared to that of the comparison photographs indicates the direction (toward or away from earth) in which the observed body is moving. Applying the Doppler principle also makes it possible to calculate the velocity V by use of the following formula:

$$V = 186,000 \frac{\lambda - \lambda_0}{\lambda_0} \text{ miles per second,}$$

where λ (lambda) is the observed wavelength and λ_0 is the true wavelength as seen on the comparison photograph. The radial velocity and direction of many thousands of stars and galaxies have been determined in this manner.

---

* Degrees kelvin may be converted to degrees fahrenheit by the formula $\frac{9}{5}$ (K–273) + 32.

2.6   RADIO ASTRONOMY

Optical telescopes are useful in gathering light from celestial bodies. The development of optical telescopes has culminated in the construction of the 200-inch Hale telescope on Mount Palomar. As we have noted, it is problematical whether a larger telescope would add appreciably to the efficiency of viewing, since unsteady atmospheric conditions become more troublesome as telescope size increases. However, light represents only a narrow segment of the electromagnetic spectrum whereas radiation covers a much broader range of frequencies. Furthermore, many of the light frequencies are filtered out by the atmosphere and are difficult to detect. A portion of the radio band of the electromagnetic spectrum does find a *window* in the atmosphere through which radiation from distant objects reaches the earth's surface. This band is limited to radiation with a wavelength of 0.25 centimeters (0.1 inch) to about 30 meters (33 yards). Radio waves longer than this are reflected into space by the ionosphere, and shorter wavelengths are absorbed by the atmosphere.

The fact that radio waves reach the earth from outer space was discovered accidentally in 1932 by Karl Jansky, a Bell Telephone scientist. He was studying the nature of radio static and found that even during periods of atmospheric calm when no lightning was flashing, there was still a persistent hiss in his receiver. This noise seemed to follow a regular cycle reaching a peak every day. Jansky finally concluded that the source of the disturbance came from radio waves originating beyond the sun. He was unable to define the source of this radiation more definitely, and for a long time it was thought that these radio waves came from the hydrogen which fills the space between the stars. Little was done about this discovery because equipment capable of relating celestial objects with the radio signals was unavailable. During World War II, sensitive equipment was developed for detecting radar signals and these tools provided a means of studying radio waves from space.

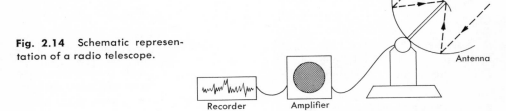

Fig. 2.14   Schematic representation of a radio telescope.

Recorder   Amplifier   Antenna

Radio telescopes function in the same manner as optical telescopes. However, they collect radio energy and detect the source of this energy whereas optical telescopes gather light. The antenna is the large parabolic dish characteristic of a radio telescope. It may be compared to the objective mirror of a reflecting telescope, since radio waves are reflected to focus on a small antenna (Fig. 2.14). The radio signals are first fed to an amplifier and then to recording equipment for either an audio or a visual record. Radio telescopes must be made as large as possible because the amount of radio energy striking the earth's surface is quite small, being somewhere around 100 watts. Because only a very small fraction of this signal is intercepted by the *dish,* amplification is necessary if it is to be recorded.

One disadvantage of the radio telescope is its inability to resolve small details within a few minutes of arc. This is because the radio wavelength is much greater than the wavelength of visual light. The resolving ability is, therefore, dependent on the diameter of the antenna and the wavelength of radiation being observed. Another disadvantage is the antenna's tendency to pick up unwanted signals from thunderstorms and electrical equipment.

The radio telescope also has certain advantages. Because the wavelengths of radio energy are large, the parabolic antenna need not have the precision required in an optical telescope. The cross section of a very large antenna may deviate from an exact parabola by as much as a foot. This tolerance greatly simplifies the construction of a 600-foot-diameter antenna. While viewing is limited to night for the optical telescopes and then is frequently poor, these handicaps do not apply to the radio telescope. It may be used whenever desired, in daytime or during overcast weather, since radio waves are not influenced by these factors (Fig. 2.15).

One of the earliest findings made by radio telescope was the fact that sun was a strong source of radio signals, especially during periods of high sunspot and flare activity. The intensity of the signals was much reduced when the sunspot and flare activity decreased. The planet Jupiter is also responsible for considerable activity, and this is surprising since it does not generate energy as the sun does. Enormous energies are involved, and the problem will not be solved until a space probe to Jupiter is successfully achieved. Discrete sources of radio waves outside the solar system number more than 2000. These were formerly known as radio stars but in most cases stars are not involved. The first true radio star, discovered in 1961, is invisible to the unaided eye and is known as 3G–48. The Crab Nebula, the gaseous remains of an exploding supernova, is a strong source of radio waves. This nebula, visible with an optical telescope, is expanding at the fantastic rate of almost three million miles an hour. The high turbulence of the gases and the high temperature is thought to be responsible for the generation of radio waves. Exploding stars observed by Tycho Brahe in 1572 and Johannes Kepler in 1604 are also sources of radio emissions. Regions of diffuse gases within the Milky Way are sources of radio waves also, and have been an important factor in studies concerned with the shape of the galaxy. Extragalactic sources of radio emissions have been detected, some of which have been identified as colliding galaxies. Such an event, 700 million light-years away, was detected in the constellation of Cygnus by means of a radio telescope and photographed with the 200-inch Hale telescope. Even more recently the mysterious quasars have been discovered.

2.7   ADDITIONAL ASTRONOMICAL TOOLS

Radar, developed during World War II for detecting the presence of distant objects on our planet, has been adapted to astronomical uses. While telescopes receive light or radio waves in certain frequencies, radar sends out radio impulses and records the echo received when the radio beam is reflected from some distant object. This technique has been used to measure the distance to nearby celestial objects within the solar system. The first attempt was made in 1946 when the U.S. Army reflected radar off the moon and measured the time necessary for the signal to return. Since radio waves travel at the speed of light, it is possible to measure distances such as this with high precision. Since then the distances to the sun and nearby planets have also been measured by radar.

Fig. 2.15 The new 210-foot in diameter tracking and communication antenna of the world-wide NASA/JPL Deep Space Network, is stationed in the high desert near Goldstone, California. The massive dish and its pedestal weigh 8000 tons. The new dish is the world's most powerful tracking and communication instrument. [Courtesy of Jet Propulsion Laboratory, NASA.]

The use of radar is limited to the solar system, however, because the radar beam is so widely scattered when striking a rough surface that the returning echo is very faint.

A development more recent than radar is the laser beam. Laser (Light Amplification by Stimulated Emission of Radiation) is a device for sending out a beam of light through a synthetic ruby. All the rays in the light beam are parallel and in phase, so there is little interference and scattering of the light. By aiming the laser, the operator can send a narrow beam of light toward some distant object. This technique was first applied in 1962, with the moon as the target. A light impulse of duration $\frac{1}{2000}$ of a second was sent toward the moon every minute. The light beam had a diameter of about one mile when it had completed its journey to the moon and back. The reflected light signals were detected approximately 2.56 seconds after they left the earth.

One major problem encountered by astronomers in using optical or radio telescopes is the interference caused by electromagnetic radiation in the atmosphere. The atmosphere is responsible for refracting, reflecting, and filtering radiation of all sorts, thus reducing the effectiveness of astronomical instruments. Turbulence in the atmosphere affects viewing with the optical telescope and becomes a greater problem with the larger instruments. Recent advantages in technology and engineering have presented possible solutions in the form of instrument-carrying rockets and satellites. Balloons, carrying small telescopes and other instruments, had been used with some success in the past but they were limited to an elevation of less than twenty miles. Rockets have extended this elevation to several hundred miles, and artificial satellites and space vehicles have made further probes possible. Successful probes to the moon, Venus, and Mars have provided invaluable data unobtainable with equipment used on the earth. Sensitive devices capable of detecting cosmic radiation, meteor activity, temperature, and magnetic fields have been developed and successfully used, as well as television equipment for transmitting pictures through space back to earth (Fig. 2.15).

All this equipment would be useless if the telemetry system, capable of receiving and decoding messages from earth and encoding and transmitting data to the earth, were not available. Equipment probes will soon be followed by manned probes, and man himself will explore the nearby planets where feasible. It is probable that in the near future a station established on the airless moon will include an observatory from which uninterrupted viewing will yield many valuable data on the nature of the universe.

2.8 SUMMARY

Almost all that is known of distant objects has been learned by studying the light received from these objects. Since the invention of the telescope more than 350 years ago, increased attention has been given to improving the gathering and analyzing of light. Newton's work with the spectrum led to the eventual discovery by Kirchhoff that lines on the spectrum represented a *signature* of the elements. This discovery had a profound effect on the science of astronomy, for it led astronomers to the realization that very distant objects were of essentially the same composition as the earth and its neighbors.

Many improvements have been made on the telescope since its invention, both to extend its range and to increase the quality of the image. Chromatic aberration, one of the first problems encountered by Galileo with his refracting telescope, was solved by Newton's reflecting telescope. By combining glass of different types, John Dolland later was able to reduce chromatic aberration to some degree in the refracting telescope, which permitted the more effective use of larger objective lenses and extended the range of the instrument. The ultimate in refracting telescopes was the 40-inch telescope located at Yerkes Observatory in Wisconsin. This refracting telescope with its large objective lens, which can be supported only at the rim, is probably of the maximum practical size. On the other hand, the mirror of a reflecting telescope which may be supported on all surfaces except the reflecting surface, places no size limitation on the instrument itself. However, increasing the size of a mirror beyond that of the 200-inch Mount Palomar telescope may restrict the field of view to impractical limits and increase the problem of atmospheric disturbance.

Light represents only a small segment of electromagnetic radiation. For this reason, since World War II radio telescopes have played an increasingly greater role in the search for new knowledge of the universe. The radio telescope is capable of collecting invisible electromagnetic wavelengths. The interpretation of these data has led to important discoveries. The use of radar and laser beams is relatively new. Their full potentials have not yet been realized.

SUGGESTED READINGS

HILTNER, W. A., ed., *Astronomical Techniques.* Chicago: University of Chicago Press, 1962.
KING, H. C., *The History of the Telescope.* London: Charles Griffin, 1955.
MICZAIKA, G. R., and W. M. SINTON, *Tools of the Astronomer.* Cambridge, Mass.: Harvard University Press, 1961.
STEINBERG, J. L., and J. LEQUEUX, *Radio Astronomy,* trans. by R. N. Bracewell, New York: McGraw-Hill, 1963.

CHAPTER 3

THE SOLAR SYSTEM

Through the past 2500 years, thinking about the solar system has evolved from considering it an earth-centered structure to the present concept of celestial bodies revolving around the sun. With the invention of the telescope, additional planets were discovered and added to the group already known.

3.1 ORGANIZATION OF THE SOLAR SYSTEM

The solar system is made up of thousands of particles and bodies varying in size from the sun, which makes up about 99% of the mass of the solar system, down to the fine particles of dust floating in interplanetary space. Aside from the sun, the nine known planets are the other major bodies found in the solar system. These range from Mercury, the closest to the sun, at 36 million miles, to Pluto, the most distant, at 3700 million miles from the sun.

Under the Copernican system, Mercury, Venus, Mars, Jupiter, and Saturn maintained their status as planets. The earth was added to this group of objects that revolved around the sun, and the moon became an earth satellite rather than a planet. With the aid of the telescope, Uranus was discovered and added to the group in 1781 and Neptune in 1846. Pluto, the outermost planet, was discovered in 1930 completing the list of nine known principal planets. Meanwhile in 1801, Ceres, the largest of the asteroids, or minor planets, was discovered in an orbit between Mars and Jupiter, and many more asteroids have been discovered in this part of the solar system since that time. Neither the planets nor the asteroids have a source of light of their own. They are visible only because of reflected sunlight.

The organization of the planets with respect to the sun follows a pattern surviving from the time the solar system was created. The orbits of all the planets are slightly elliptical and the planets are nearly all on the same plane. This ecliptic plane, as it is called, is formed by the extension of an imaginary line from the sun to the orbiting earth. Most planetary orbits vary only a few degrees, but Pluto is an exception, varying 17° from the ecliptic plane.

The direction of motion is also a property which members of the solar system have in common. The revolutions of the planets are from west to east across the sky, as seen from the earth. If the solar system is viewed from the direction of the polar star (Polaris) all the planets revolve around the sun in a counterclockwise direction. This has also been found to be the direction of most satellites around their respective planets and the most common direction of rotation of all planets on their axes.

In the middle of the eighteenth century, Titius of Wittenberg developed a simple mathematical rule which gave the approximate distances from the known planets to the sun. This rule was much publicized by a Berlin astronomer, Johann Bode, and became known as Bode's Law although it is neither a law nor a theory. It is a sequence of numbers obtained by starting with zero and following with 3, 6, 12, etc., doubling each subsequent number. Four is then added to each of these numbers, and the sum divided by 10 gives the mean distance of the planets from the sun in astronomical units.

As has been previously stated, one astronomical unit is equal to the mean distance from the earth to the sun or 92,956,200 ± 300 miles. This figure is usually rounded off to a more convenient 93 million miles. Kepler had measured the distance of the planets to the sun in astronomical units, but the first attempt to measure this distance in miles was made by French astronomers in 1672. In that year, Mars was close to the earth and directly opposite the earth from the sun. The parallactic displacement of Mars as seen from Paris and French Guiana was 9.5 seconds of arc (Fig. 3.1). On the basis of this measurement, the astronomical unit was calculated to be 87 million miles.

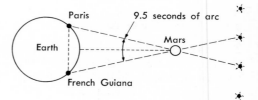

Fig. 3.1 In 1672 French observers measured the length of the astronomical unit by making simultaneous observations from Paris and French Guiana.

This method had the disadvantage of requiring two observers working some distance from each other. In 1877 David Gill made use of the earth's rotation as a substitute for spatial separation. On Ascension Island he made paired observations, twelve hours apart, of Mars during a five-month period (Fig. 3.2). The results were excellent, giving a distance of about 93 million miles from the earth to the sun. This distance has been confirmed many times by observations with improved techniques.

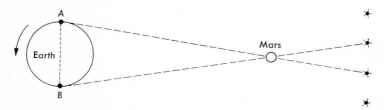

Fig. 3.2 The method used by Gill to measure the astronomical unit took advantage of the rotation of the earth. The method involved making paired observations of Mars, first at A and 12 hours later at B.

At the time Bode presented his law no planet was known at 2.8 *AU,* a figure occurring in the sequence of numbers between those representing distances from the sun to Mars and Jupiter. Bode suggested that a search be made for another planet. When Uranus was discovered in 1781 at 19.2 *AU,* in satisfactory agreement with the series, much strength was lent to his law and a search for a missing planet was begun. This search lead to the discovery of the asteroid Ceres by Piazzi in 1801, at approximately 2.8 *AU.* Since that time hundreds of other asteroids have been discovered in the same general orbit.

TABLE 3.1

	Bode's Law	Astronomical units	Millions of miles
Mercury	0.4	0.39	36
Venus	0.7	0.72	67
Earth	1.0	1.00	93
Mars	1.6	1.52	142
Ceres	2.8	2.77	257
Jupiter	5.2	5.20	483
Saturn	10.0	9.58	886
Uranus	19.6	19.19	1782
Neptune	38.8	30.17	2793
Pluto	77.2	39.46	3670

The exceptions to Bode's Law are the two outermost planets Neptune and Pluto. Some astronomers account for this by saying that Pluto was once a satellite of Neptune's which escaped and caused the variance in their orbital distances to the sun.

Table 3.1 shows a comparison between Bode's Law and the actual distances of the planets in astronomical units and in miles.

3.2   FORMATION OF THE SOLAR SYSTEM

Although the structure and organization of the solar system were fairly well established in the early eighteenth century, no attempt had been made to theorize on the possible means of its formation. Even men like Newton considered that the universe was immutable and that the small measurable changes taking place were all cyclic and part of a stable cosmos. By the middle of the eighteenth century, however, several ideas were suggested to account for the formation of the solar system.

In 1749 a French naturalist, G. Buffon, theorized that the planets were formed as a result of a collision between a comet and the sun. The theory that this event scattered material which formed the planets became known as the *Close-Encounter Hypothesis.* In 1900 T. C. Chamberlain and F. R. Moulton of the University of Chicago modified this idea, suggesting that a visiting star passed so close to the sun that material was drawn from the sun, forming the planets. If this were what occurred, then the solar system would be unique in the universe, since celestial collisions are extremely rare. It is now believed, however, that the planets and the other bodies in the solar system were formed as a natural step in the sun's evolution. This process has probably been repeated many times in the universe, with the result that there are many stars accompanied by planets. Because of problems which cannot be satisfactorily explained on the basis of the Close-Encounter theory, it has been discarded.

Another theory no longer considered seriously is the *Binary-Star Hypothesis.* According to this theory, the sun was once one of a pair of stars, a circumstance not unusual in the universe. It proposes that a visiting star or some other phenomenon led to the disintegration of the second star, and that part of the debris remained under the sun's gravitational influence to form the planets.

At present the *Nebular Hypothesis* prevails as the most probable explanation of how the solar system was formed. It was first suggested in 1753 by the philosopher Immanuel Kant and then put in more precise astronomical terms in 1796 by the French astronomer and mathematician Pierre Simon LaPlace.

The original form of the theory presumed that the solar system was created from a vast cloud of gas. As the gas cooled and contracted, its speed of rotation increased. Bulging at the center as the gases coalesced, a ring was abandoned by the contracting mass. Successively smaller rings were subsequently left behind, each forming a gas globe which had a circular orbit around the main mass. The main mass, which contained most of the material, formed the sun.

This theory leaves much to be desired because it is known that gases tend to disperse rather than coalesce. All but abandoned, the theory was modified by C. F. von Weizsäcker after World War II and later by G. P. Kuiper. In its modified form the theory removes some of the objections. The cloud was presumably made up of gas, mainly hydrogen and helium, and dust particles of the heavier elements. Gravitational attraction, light pressure from other stars, and the effect of rotation resulted in the formation of a lens-shaped body. The intense heat, generated at the center of the mass by gravitational compression, finally triggered a thermonuclear reaction, and the sun was born. The rotating disk of gas and dust that remained was in a high state of turbulence and broke up into eddies of the irregular size. The size of the eddies tended to increase toward the outer zones. Thse eddies are sometimes referred to as *protoplanets*. The small particles collided, gradually forming larger and larger bodies which swept up more and more material eventually to form the planets. The heat within the planets themselves was produced by gravitational compression and radioactive decay within the mass. Some believe the planets were originally in a molten state. Others feel that the planets were relatively cool when formed and heated up internally as they increased in size and with passage of time.

This theory, at present, finds the greatest acceptance among astronomers. However, it is probably not the last word on the formation of the solar system.

3.3   AGE OF THE SOLAR SYSTEM

How long ago were the earth and the solar system formed? The system is very complex yet it has many common characteristics which would indicate that the solar system was formed at one time rather than in piecemeal fashion. Measuring the rate of radioactive decay of certain elements for example, the decay from uranium to lead or from strontium to rubidium, has provided a method for determining the age of rocks. The oldest rock formed on the surface of the earth was found to be about 3.3 billion years old. This is then the youngest that the earth could be since the rock must be formed before the elements can begin radioactive decay. Measurements on stony meteorites similar in composition to the mantle of the earth reveal an age of about 4.5 billion years. Because of the similarities it may be presumed that the meteorites were formed at the same time as the stony mantle and iron core of the earth. It probably took millions of years for the relatively cool earth to heat up sufficiently from radioactivity to permit the mantle and core to separate. Therefore, the 4.5 billion years is perhaps a lower limit for the age of the earth. If the length of time necessary for the protoplanet to form into the planet is considered, then the age of the earth approaches perhaps 5 billion years.

The sun's formation is thought to have taken place about 1 billion years prior to the formation of the earth, making the age of the solar system about 6 billion years.

3.4 CONSTITUENTS OF THE SOLAR SYSTEM

Determining the physical properties of the various members of the solar system has been a difficult task because of the great distances involved. Despite this difficulty, a surprising amount of information has been gathered which is a tribute to the diligence and patience of the many people involved in this pursuit.

The Sun. During the height of the ancient Greek civilization, the sun was viewed as a huge flaming rock about the size of Greece. It is a unique body in the solar system by contrast with the cold unlighted bodies surrounding it, being 864,600 miles in diameter and comprising about 99% of the mass of material in the solar system. The sun is of interest because its mass governs the movement of all the other members of the solar system and its radiation is the primary source of energy in the solar system. The sun, appearing large because it is close to the earth, is actually a star and, for this reason, yields much information on the nature of stars in general.

The sun is not by any extent the most important star. Others are vastly greater in size as, for instance, Betelgeuse, which has a volume 27 million times that of the sun. Actually, it is so large that the earth could revolve through its orbit entirely within the body of Betelgeuse. On the other hand, many stars are smaller than the sun. Some are 100,000 times as bright as the sun, some are $\frac{1}{10,000}$ as bright. The sun could, on this basis, be considered a typical average star.

Because of the high temperatures, the sun is essentially gaseous in nature. The bulk of this gas is hydrogen with a small amount of helium and a fraction of a percent of the heavier elements. Of the 92 naturally occurring elements, 70 have been identified on the sun. None have been found on the sun which do not exist on the earth although helium was discovered on the sun in 1868 and was not found on the earth until 27 years later.

Only the surface temperature of the sun can be measured with any degree of accuracy, and by means of several methods it was found to be about 10,400°F at the center of the sun's disk. The temperature is about 500°F less at the sun's edge, or limb, because radiation toward the earth passes through a thicker layer of gases at the limbs than in the center (Fig. 3.3). The temperature of the interior cannot be measured directly but has been theoretically calculated on a number of occasions. Temperatures of 20,000,-000 to 40,000,000°F have been suggested on the basis of the rate at which pressure, temperature, and density increase as the center of the sun is approached.

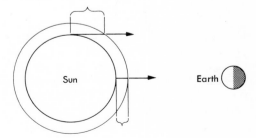

Fig. 3.3 Radiation going toward the earth, E, from the sun, S, must pass through thicker layers of gas in the sun's atmosphere at the limbs or edge of the sun than at the center. (Diagram is not to scale.)

Among the more interesting features of the sun are the *sunspots* first seen by Scheiner and then Galileo through a telescope. The movement of the sunspots was the first evidence that the sun rotated on its axis. By careful observation, astronomers found that all parts of the sun do not rotate at the same speed. The sun's equator rotates once in about 25 days, while the speed of rotation is 28 days at a latitude halfway to the polar areas and about 34 days at the poles. This variation in the speed of rotation is additional evidence that the sun is made of gaseous material.

Sunspots vary in size, most being relatively small, 1000 miles in diameter, and lasting only a few days, while a few may reach a diameter of many thousands of miles and last several weeks. Sunspots have a dark center, the *umbra,* and a lighter edge, the *penumbra.* The center of a sunspot is not truly black but is dark by comparison to the surrounding area of the dazzlingly bright sun. The temperature of a sunspot is about 2000°F lower than the normal surface of the sun, but nevertheless considerably hotter and brighter than an electric arc lamp.

In the early part of the nineteenth century, a German druggist, Heinrich Schwabe, who had a great interest in astronomy began keeping a systematic record of the sun's surface. He was looking for the planet Vulcan, purported to be in an orbit between Mercury and the sun. No such planet existed, but Schwabe's detailed record eventually led him to the discovery of the cyclic nature of sunspot occurrence. He found that sunspot activity from minimum to maximum and back to minimum took a period of about 10 to 11 years. He announced his findings in 1843 but was to work another 10 to 15 years before his efforts were recognized. Later it was found that the sunspots varied in position on the sun as the cycle progressed. As the new cycle started at minimum a few spots would appear about 30° north and south of the equator. As the cycle progressed, new spots appeared but closer to the equator until, at maximum activity, most sunspots appeared in a zone around 15° north and south of the equator. At the end of the cycle, a few spots appeared from 5° to 10° above and below the equator, while, at the same time, a few spots appeared 30° from the equator. This situation signaled the start of a new cycle. The reason for the cyclic nature of sunspot activity is not known. However, if the cycle of activity continues as in the past, then the minimum activity in 1964 means that the maximum level will be reached in about 1969, and the minimum level again in 1974 or 1975.

In 1908 further investigation on the properties of sunspots led George Hale of the Mount Wilson observatory to the conclusion that sunspots had a magnetic field. Hale made use of a discovery by Pieter Zeeman in 1896. Zeeman had found that the spectrum lines of glowing sodium vapor broadened when a tube of glowing vapor was placed between the poles of an electromagnet. The normally single spectrum lines became double or triple under the influence of the magnetic field. This became known as the *Zeeman effect.* Hale observed this effect in light from sunspots. By means of a polarizing attachment on the spectroscope Hale was then able to show that the leading spots in a group had a positive polarity, and the trailing spots had a negative polarity. He also found that sunspot groups in the northern and southern hemispheres had opposite polarities. With the start of a new cycle, the polarities in both hemispheres were reversed, thus indicating that the point of minimum sunspot activity was the real start of each new cycle. If the polarity of sunspots were considered along with sunspot activity, then the length of the cycle would be 22 years. The reason for the reversal of polarity is not known.

Solar *prominences* are another phenomenon of the sun and are best visible along the limb during a total eclipse, when the main body of the sun is covered. Before 1860 they were thought to be actual appendages of the moon since they could be seen only during an eclipse. Since then, special equipment has been devised to enable observers to see prominences at any time.

Prominences may be described as great sheets of flame which rise tens of thousands of miles above the sun's surfaces at speeds of up to 450 miles per second. They appear to be more numerous with greater sunspot activity, although not all prominences are associated with or caused by sunspot activity. Prominences are classified into a number of different types according to the kind of activity and the shape they display. No really workable theory has been presented to explain the cause of the prominences or the variation in their motion.

Another characteristic part of the sun is the *corona,* seen only during a total eclipse or with specialized equipment which blanks out the sun's disk. The corona is an extensive and extremely rarified gaseous envelope surrounding the sun, reaching hundreds of thousands of miles into space. Its light is only about one-half that of the moon and is completely masked by the sun's brilliance. The temperature of the corona is about 2,000,000°F. Its presence is thought to be in some way related to sunspot activity.

The enormous amount of energy released by the sun is the primary source of energy on earth. Early man, viewing the sun probably concluded that the warmth was the result of a burning process, but nothing could be further from the truth. Burning or combustion, as it is understood on earth, is a process involving the break-down of organic compounds in the presence of oxygen, a resulting release of energy, and the formation of carbon dioxide. While oxygen and carbon are to be found on the sun, the temperature of the sun is far too hot to allow these elements to combine. Carbon is thought to be involved in the release of energy in massive stars and to a very small degree in the sun, but not in the manner described above. Since compounds or combinations of elements cannot exist on the sun because of the high temperature, the sun is made up of a mixture of atoms of the various elements and subatomic particles.

The atom, then, is the actual source of energy on the sun or, more precisely, the binding energy of the atomic nucleus. Einstein established a mass-energy relationship with the formula $E = mc^2$, where E represents the energy of mass m and c is a constant equal to the speed of light. Because c^2 is such a large number, a small amount of mass will release a tremendous amount of energy. For example, one gram of matter could theoretically yield the amount of energy obtained by burning more than 3000 tons of coal in the conventional manner.

There are two possible means whereby energy bound up in the atom could be released: *nuclear fission* and *nuclear fusion.* In the nuclear fission process, a heavy element is broken down into two lighter elements whose combined mass is slightly less than the mass of the original element. The difference in mass is energy which is released as in an atomic bomb. The heavy elements required for this type of reaction are not available on the sun. However, there is an abundance of hydrogen which makes the fusion process the likely mechanism for the release of energy. In this process, hydrogen nuclei are combined to form helium through a series of reactions called the proton-proton chain. The first step in the reaction is the fusing of two protons into deuteron or heavy hydrogen isotopes and the emission of a positron:

$$_1H^1 + _1H^1 \longrightarrow _1H^2 + _1e^0.$$

The positron subsequently combines with an electron to form a gamma ray. The deuteron encounters and combines with another proton to form a light helium isotope:

$$_1H^2 + {_1}H^1 \longrightarrow {_2}H^3.$$

Two light helium isotopes fuse to form a stable helium atom and two protons:

$$_2H^3 + {_2}H^3 \qquad {_2}H^4 + 2{_1}H^1.$$

Each of these reactions results in the release of a small amount of energy which is represented by the loss in mass. Four hydrogen atoms (or protons), each with an atomic weight of 1.008 and a combined atomic weight of 4.032, will yield one helium atom with an atomic weight of 4.003. The difference in mass provides the energy radiated by the sun.

The total amount of energy radiated by the sun, or its luminosity, can be determined by measuring the strength of the solar radiation received on the earth's surface. In making such a measurement, energy absorbed or reflected by the earth's atmosphere must be taken into account. Careful studies have shown that the amount of energy striking the earth is 1.97 cal/cm²/min or 1.37×10^6 ergs/cm²/sec, which is known as the solar constant. Since it can be assumed that the sun radiates uniformly in all directions, the total amount of energy given off by the sun should be the solar constant multiplied by the surface area of a sphere with a radius of 1 AU. This area is equal to 2.82×10^{27} cm², so the total output of energy by the sun is 3.8×10^{33} ergs/sec. This is energy which has been formed at the expense of some of the sun's mass.

How much mass is being expended can be determined by again making use of Einstein's formula, $E = mc^2$. The energy (E) output per second is known, and c is the speed of light. From this, the mass (m) can be calculated. It is found that more than 4.6 million tons of matter are converted into energy every second. As large as this rate may be it has very little effect on the sun's activity. In a year, the sun loses by radiation about one 15,000-billionth of its total mass, but this does not mean that the sun will last for 15,000 billion years, because it will not continue to function in its present manner to complete annihilation. Since only about 0.7% of the mass in the hydrogen to helium conversion becomes energy, the sun has a theoretical life expectancy of about 100 billion years. This figure is too large, however, because the temperature at the center of the sun necessary for continuance of this reaction cannot be maintained after about 10% of the available fuel has been exhausted. A realistic life expectancy for the sun is, therefore, about 10 to 11 billion years. The age of the sun is now about 6 billion years; hence the sun's eventual demise is predicted for some 4 or 5 billion years in the future.

The Planets.   While the sun is the source of energy and controlling force in the solar system, the planets are of interest because they are bodies which can be identified with the earth. Much of what is known about the planets that is of a statistical nature may readily be shown in tabular form for convenience (Table 3.2).

Mercury.   This planet, named after the messenger of the gods, is closest to the sun and has the shortest period of revolution. Observations of surface features on the planet and careful calculations made in 1965 by T. Gold have made it possible to determine that the period of rotation is 59 ± 3 days while the period of revolution is 88 days.

Temperatures up to 770°F have been measured on the bright side, a temperature hot enough to melt lead and sulfur. By contrast, the side facing away from the sun is extremely cold, with temperatures as low as −400°F.

TABLE 3.2

	Mercury	Venus	Earth	Mars	Jupiter	Saturn	Uranus	Neptune	Pluto
Discovery	ancient	ancient	—	ancient	ancient	ancient	Hershel, 1781	Adams, Leverrier, Galle, 1846	Tombaugh 1930
Diameter (in miles)	3100	7570	7927	4200	88,600	75,100	29,300	27,700	3600
Period of rotation	59 ±3 days	unknown	24 hr	24 hr 37 min	9 hr, 50 min	10 hr, 14 min	10 hr, 45 min	12 hr, 48 min	6.5 days
Period of revolution	88 days	225 days	365¼ days	687 days	11.9 yr	29.5 yr	84.0 yr	164.8 yr	248.4 yr
Atmosphere	none	extensive	extensive	thin	extensive	extensive	probably extensive	probably extensive	unknown
Temperature (degrees Fahrenheit)	−400 to 700	800	50	−50 to 50	−216	−243	−300	−330	
Satellites	none	none	1	2	12	10	5	2	

An atmosphere such as occurs on earth is practically nonexistent. Only very heavy gases may remain on Mercury. The remainder of the gases would be lost in space because of the low gravitational attraction of this small planet or would be trapped in a liquid or solid form on the dark side where the temperature is low.

The mean distance of Mercury from the sun, as previously stated, is 36 million miles. However, its orbit is elliptical so that the distance to the sun is 43.5 million miles at *aphelion* (point in orbit at greatest distance from the sun) and 28.5 million miles at *perihelion* (closest approach to the sun).

Venus. Named for the goddess of beauty, Venus is sometimes called the earth's twin because of a similarity in size. It appears in the sky in extreme brightness due to reflection of sunlight from clouds which completely enshroud this planet. The clouds have made it impossible to view any of the surface features of Venus, despite the fact that Venus comes within 26 million miles of the earth, closer than any other planet.

In the past the nature of the surface of Venus was completely unknown and the atmosphere was assumed to be clouds of water vapor similar to the clouds on earth. The surface of Venus was pictured as being a damp, swampy jungle. When it was found that the clouds were not water vapor the surface was featured as a dry, hot desert with hurricane-like winds blowing dust high into the atmosphere. The fact that high concentrations of carbon dioxide were formed in the atmosphere troubled some astronomers. Carbon dioxide in great quantities exists on the earth but is tied up in carbonate rock. Why was this not so on Venus? Possibly, it it was suggested, because the entire surface of Venus is covered with water. One fault with this theory is that surface temperatures were thought to be at least 600°F, which would result in the boiling away of any existing oceans. However, this would account for the tremendous cloud formation.

The Mariner II probe, launched from Cape Kennedy on August 27, 1962 has yielded some information about Venus which changed some of the previous views. Data from this probe show that the rotation rate may be longer than the period of revolution, about 230 days ± 40 to 50 days. Because of this slow rate, the rotation may actually be retrograde with the sun rising in the west and setting in the east approximately once each revolution around the sun. Neither a magnetic field nor a radiation belt similar to the Van Allen belt around the earth was found at the 21,600-mile approach of the probe.

The layer of clouds around Venus was found to be about 15 miles thick, starting about 45 miles from the Venusian surface and extending to an altitude of about 60 miles. Temperatures at the base of the cloud layer are about 200°F and at the cloud surface about −30°F. The atmosphere probably contains high amounts of nitrogen, carbon dioxide, and small concentrations of oxygen.

Surface temperatures on Venus were determined to be about 800°F on both the light and dark sides. The surface appears to be rough, and its reflectivity is equal to that of dust and sand. No water could exist at these temperatures, but some pools of molten metal may be present.

More recently a balloon probe carried a telescope 16 miles above the earth's surface, high enough to be above moisture and dust in our atmosphere. Spectroscopic examination of Venus' cloud layer in this instance showed a remarkable similarity to ice-crystal clouds high in the earth's atmosphere. These ice-crystal clouds, it was suggested, would reflect a great deal of the sun's energy. Therefore, the surface temperatures of Venus may be comparatively cool, possibly as cool as the higher temperatures on the surface of the earth. Scientists studying cloud activity on earth find that turbulent clouds give off radiations. This turbulence in the Venusian atmosphere may be interpreted as high temperatures on the planet's surface. Future probes will, no doubt, be sent to investigate these mysteries.

Earth.   The earth is the third planet from the sun and, as far as is known, the only one in the solar system that is inhabited. It is possible to interpret data obtained from other planets as to conditions on these planets because the physical laws of science which apply on earth are assumed to apply in all parts of the universe. There is some problem in studying the earth in its entirety because only a small portion is visible at any one time to a single observer on the surface. Certain aspects could be viewed better by an observer on Venus or Mars. From those vantage points it would be relatively easy to view the physical shape and astronomical motion of the planet earth.

Recent measurements have shown that the earth is not a perfect sphere as the Greeks thought. It is an oblate spheroid, slightly compressed at the poles and bulging at the equator as a result of the earth's rotation. Several other small irregularities have been discovered as a result of satellite measurements. It was found that a cross section of the earth at the equator was not circular but slightly elliptical. Furthermore it was established that for corresponding latitudes the southern hemisphere bulged more than the northern hemisphere, resulting, to a small extent, in a pear-shaped earth.

The polar diameter of the earth, currently recognized by the International Union of Geodesy and Geophysics, is 7902 miles, and the equatorial diameter is 7927 miles. The circumference at the equator is about 24,907 miles. Measuring the diameter and circumference of the earth is not a recent accomplishment. In the third century B.C., a Greek astronomer, Eratosthenes, was able to measure the circumference of the earth. He noted that on the longest day of the year in Alexandria, a stake in the ground cast a shadow of slightly over 7° of arc at noon (Fig. 3.4). On the same day in Syene (Aswan), the sun was directly overhead and cast no shadow. The angular difference between the location of the two cities was 1/50 of a complete circle and the distance between the two cities was 5000 stadia (575 miles). From these facts, he calculated the circumference of the earth and found it to be equivalent to 28,750 miles. This estimate is somewhat higher than the present-day figure, but Eratosthenes did not have the advantage of modern precision equipment.

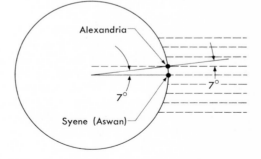

Fig. 3.4 Eratosthenes' method of measuring the circumference of the earth.

An observer on a neighboring planet would be able to detect the presence of an atmosphere around the earth. This atmosphere is a layer of gases which surrounds the earth to a height of about 500 miles. The exact height is difficult to determine because the higher the altitude the more rarefied the atmosphere becomes.

The movement of the earth within the solar system takes several forms that can be easily recognized. Daily rotation around the axis results in daylight and darkness as the earth's surface swings facing the sun and away from the sun. This motion also is responsible for the direction of the prevailing winds, the spinning of cyclones, and the slight bulge at the equator. The rotation of the earth has been used as a means of telling time, each rotation being equivalent to one day or 24 hours. Now it is known that the rate of rotation is not precise. Over an extended period, however, the minor variations average out.

The earth's revolution around the sun is used as a measure for one year. It requires 365¼ days to make one complete orbit. For this reason, three years of four have 365 days, and the fourth year (leap year) has 366 to compensate for the accumulated quarter days.

The precession of the earth, a movement not so readily discernible, resembles the gyrations of a spinning top or gyro. This movement is so slow that it is barely visible even to close observation and only over long periods of time. The axis of the earth is inclined 23½° from an imaginary axis perpendicular to the ecliptic plane. Precession is the movement of the axis at this angle around the imaginary axis perpendicular to the ecliptic plane. This movement causes a shifting of the earth's axis relative to the stars so that while Polaris is the present polar star, Alpha Draconis was the polar star in 3000 B.C., and Vega will be the polar star in 14,000 A.D. To return to the present position after a complete circle will require 26,000 years.

The Moon.   The earth is accompanied in its travels around the sun by a single satellite, the moon. The moon is 2160 miles in diameter, little more than one-fourth that of the earth. Although the moon ranks fifth in size compared to other satellites in the solar system, it is more massive compared to the earth than are the other satellites compared to their planets. Actually, the earth-moon system may be more characteristic of a double planet.

The mean distance from the center of the earth to the center of the moon is 238,857 miles or, more conveniently, 239,000 miles. It requires 1.28 second for light to travel from the moon to the earth. The moon does not revolve around earth in a perfect circle: its orbit is elliptical and slightly eccentric. At its closest approach (*perigee*), the moon is 221,463 miles from the earth and at its greatest distance (*apogee*), 252,710 miles from the earth.

Calculating the distance to the moon was first attempted by Aristarchus who also figured that the moon's diameter was about one-third that of the earth. However, the first accurate determination of the lunar distance was not made until 1751. The distance has been calculated many times since, in essentially the following manner: Measurements made in observatories in Northern Europe were combined with observations made from the Cape of Good Hope. In Fig. 3.5, *A* represents the northern observation point and *B,* the southern. Angles 1 and 4 could be measured between the moon and the zenith, a point vertically above the earth's surface at the site where the observation is made. The triangle *ABO* may be solved since sides *OA* and *OB* are known (radii of the earth), and angle *AOB* can be calculated from the latitudes of sites *A* and *B*. Thus it is possible to obtain values for angles 3 and 6 and for side *AB*. Angle 2 will be equal to the sum of angles 1 and 3 subtracted from 180°. Angle 5 may be found in the same manner, and triangle *ABM* can be solved since two angles and an included side are known. Now the value for *MO,* representing the distance from the earth to the moon, may be deter-

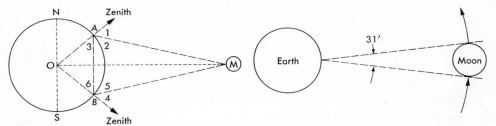

Fig. 3.5 Method used to measure the distance from the earth to the moon.

Fig. 3.6 The angular diameter of the moon as measured from the earth equals 31 seconds of arc.

mined. Modern techniques now make use of radar and laser for such measurements so that the calculated distance to the moon is quite accurate.

Once the distance from the earth to the moon is known, it is possible to find the diameter of the moon. The angular diameter of the moon has been measured and found to be 31 minutes of arc (Fig. 3.6). The distance of the earth to the moon is approximately 239,000 miles. The circumference of a circle with this radius can be calculated. A circle represents 360 degrees or $(360 \times 60) = 21,600$ minutes of arc. It is then possible to find the length of a 31-minute segment of this circle which represents the diameter of the moon:

$$\frac{2\pi r}{21,600} \times 31 \text{ or } \frac{2 \times 3.14 \times 239,000}{21,600} \times 31,$$

which is about 2160 miles.

The motion of the earth has previously been discussed without reference to the effect of the moon on this movement. What is called the earth's orbit is, in reality, the orbit of the center of mass of the earth-moon system. Slight shifts of the earth with respect to the nearest planets and the sun show that the system's center of mass is only 2895 miles from the center of earth toward the moon, so that the center of mass is actually within the earth. As a result, the earth revolves around the sun not in a straight-line but rather in a slightly wavy path (Fig. 3.7).

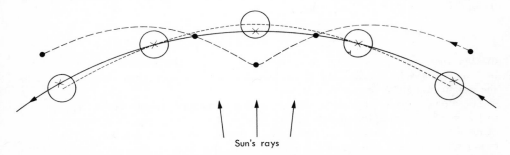

Sun's rays

Fig. 3.7 The earth and moon follow a serpentine path relative to the sun as they go around in orbit.

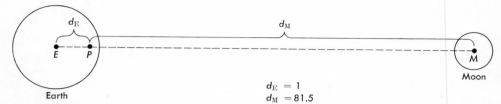

$$d_\mathrm{E} = 1$$
$$d_\mathrm{M} = 81.5$$

Fig. 3.8 The point of balance between the earth and moon is located at the center of mass of these two spheres. This point is approximately 1000 miles below the surface of the earth.

If the earth and the moon were placed at the end of a rigid stick, they could be balanced at point P (Fig. 3.8), which represents the center of mass of these two bodies. The ratio of the distance PM to PE is 81.5 to 1. If the mass of the earth were known, then the mass of the moon, could be calculated by using the following relationship:

$$m_\mathrm{E} d_\mathrm{E} = m_\mathrm{M} d_\mathrm{M},$$

where m_E and m_M are the mass of the earth and moon respectively, and d_E and d_M are the respective distances from the earth and the moon to their common center of gravity.

A number of experiments to "weigh the earth" have been performed. Jolly's method (1881) will illustrate the principle: A flask of mercury, accurately weighed, was carefully counterbalanced on a balance, and a 5-ton lead weight was placed beneath the mercury. The gravitational attraction of the lead was sufficient to offset the balanced mercury so that a small weight had to be added to counterbalance the mercury again. The distance between the centers of mass of the mercury and lead was carefully measured and the weights of these objects and the small weight added were known. These data provided the means of calculating the weight of the earth, W, from the following proportion:

$$\frac{\text{added weight} \times \mathbf{W}}{(\text{radius of earth})^2} = \frac{\text{weight of lead} \times \text{weight of mercury}}{(\text{distance between their centers})^2}.$$

In this way, the weight of the earth has been determined to be about 6.6×10^{21} tons.

The mass of the moon, m_M can now be found. The mass of the earth m_E and the proportionate distances d_E and d_M to the center of mass for these two bodies are known. Therefore

$$m_\mathrm{M} = \frac{m_\mathrm{E} d_\mathrm{E}}{d_\mathrm{M}},$$

making the moon mass about $\frac{1}{81.5}$ that of the earth. The moon's density can then be found simply by dividing the moon's weight by its volume, since density represents the weight of a given volume of matter.

The moon's revolution around the earth takes about one month. However, there are two ways of measuring the moon's period of orbit. The *sidereal month* is the true period of revolution, being the time interval between two successive conjunctions of the moon's center with the same star, as seen from the earth. The time it takes the moon to travel this 360° orbit around the earth is a sidereal month of 27 days, 7 hours, 43 minutes, 11.5 seconds, or about 27⅓ days. The *synodic month* is the interval between successive conjunctions of the moon and the sun, or from new moon to new moon. This month is longer than the sidereal month by more than 2 days, being 29 days, 12 hours, 44 minutes, 2.8 seconds or about 29½ days. The difference is due to the fact that during the moon's revolution about the earth, the earth in its turn has moved along its orbit around the sun as illustrated in Fig. 3.9. The moon's eastward motion, resulting from its movement in orbit around the earth, causes it to fall behind the movement of the earth so that the moon returns over the same meridian an average of 50 minutes later each day. This is referred to as the *daily retardation* of the moon.

The moon rotates on its axis in the same length of time in which it revolves around the earth, namely, the sidereal period of 27⅓ days. Because of this, the moon presents the same hemisphere toward the earth at all times. This means only 50% of the moon is visible to viewers on earth.

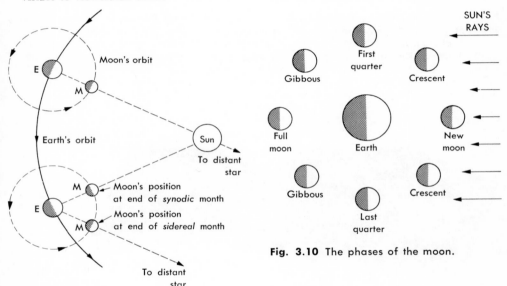

Fig. 3.10 The phases of the moon.

Fig. 3.9 The sidereal month is measured as the time it takes the moon to go 360° around the earth. The synodic month is the time it takes for the moon to make a successive conjunction with the sun, and it is slightly more than two days longer than the sidereal month.

One of the first celestial phenomena to be viewed and understood by man was the phases of the moon (Fig. 3.10). The moon itself is dark and only reflects the light from the sun as it moves around in its orbit. The alternately increasing and then decreasing lunar areas reflecting sunlight toward the earth are the phases of the moon. Because the new moon passes between the earth and the sun, the hemisphere of the moon facing the earth is dark. On the following night a slight crescent of light will appear signaling the beginning of a new lunar month. This crescent of light increases until about half the moon's sphere is lighted, when the first quarter begins. Then follows the gibbous phase: the lighted portion of the moon increases nightly until the position of the moon is opposite that of the earth from the sun and the full moon is visible. The phases are then repeated in reverse order through gibbous and last quarter to new moon again.

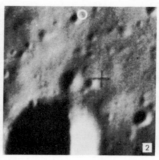

Fig. 3.11 The last three photographs taken by Camera P-1 on Ranger IX. Picture 3 was taken at an altitude of 0.68 mile, 0.453 second before impact. The impact point is circled on each photograph. The final picture covers an area 154 feet across by 125 feet from top to bottom. The impact point is on the edge of a 25-foot crater. The smallest crater visible is 2.5 feet across. Ranger IX impacted in the crater Alphonsus at 6:08:20 a.m. PST, Wednesday, March 24, 1965. North is at top where crater shadows appear at left. [Courtesy of Jet Propulsion Laboratory, NASA.]

Fig. 3.12 Composite of two narrow-angle pictures—6° field of view—taken by Surveyor I the morning of June 6, 1966, shows the crest of a small mountain range on the moon about 12 miles northeast of the spacecraft. Only the top of the small mountain shows above the near horizon which is probably less than a mile away. The observable crest of the mountain range is slightly less than 3 miles long and rises approximately 500 feet above the extension of the near horizon. This small mountain is part of the rim of a nearly buried ancient crater more than 60 miles in diameter. Surveyor I landed inside the rim. Scattered rocks in the foreground are probably associated with a crater which lies just to the right of the field of view and only a few hundred yards from the spacecraft. [Courtesy of Jet Propulsion Laboratory, NASA.]

The line between the bright and dark portions of the moon is called the *terminator.* At a casual glance, it appears as a smooth regular line, but on closer examination with magnification the line is seen to be irregular due to the mountainous nature of the lunar surface. Organisms requiring an atmosphere like those existing on the earth could not survive on the moon without special equipment because the moon has no atmosphere. No detectable gases exist on the moon. This would make it possible to get a much clearer view of other heavenly bodies from the moon than is possible from the earth.

The absence of an atmosphere is also responsible for a wide range in temperatures on the moon's surface. Temperatures vary from 215°F when the sun is at the zenith of the moon to −240°F during the lunar night. Rapid heating and cooling caused by lack of an atmosphere make existence on the moon intolerable without special protection.

The physical surface of the moon presents a rugged, desolate landscape. The smooth areas are dry plains which were called *seas* or *mares* by the early astronomers. They viewed them through their telescopes and mistook them for bodies of water. Astronomers have mapped some mountain ranges and numerous craters measuring ¼ mile to 150 miles in diameter. Although the origin of the craters is as yet unexplained, two theories have been suggested. One states that the craters are of volcanic origin formed much as the craters were on earth. The other proposes that the craters were formed by the impact of meteorites on the surface of the moon. Long, crooked narrow crevices of unknown depth similar to earthquake faults on earth are visible and are called *rills*. Light-colored streaks radiating from certain craters can be seen and are called *rays*. Rays cast no shadow, so they are not cracks or ridges. They appear to be made of material coming from the craters. Photographs made by Ranger IX and Surveyor probes (Figures 3.11, 3.12, 3.13) show details of the surface of the moon never before seen. However the photographs do not reveal the nature of the material forming the rays.

Until recently it was not possible to view the outer edges of the sun except during a total eclipse. This event made possible the examination of prominences and corona. In the pattern of movements of the sun, the earth, and the moon, there are always two to five solar eclipses during a year. Some are partial, some annular, and some total. On the average only two total eclipses occur on earth every three years.

A total eclipse of the sun can occur only when the moon is new, that is, when it is between the earth and the sun. Furthermore, it occurs only when the moon is at its nearest approach to the earth. Since the moon's shadow is 232,000 miles long, on the average, and the average distance from the moon to the earth is 239,000 miles, it is obvious that an eclipse could not occur under average conditions. However, because of its elliptical orbit the moon's shadow is sometimes longer than the distance from the moon to the earth, allowing the shadow to fall on the earth causing a total eclipse.

It is possible to see a total eclipse when the true shadow, called *umbra,* of the moon passes overhead. The umbra produces a round shadow never more than 170 miles in diameter as it travels over the earth. The *penumbra,* which surrounds the umbra like an inverted cone, does not completely hide the sun, and observers located on any point in the lightly shaded area in Fig. 3.14 will see only a partial eclipse. It forms a circle about 4000 miles in diameter.

At the moment of totality it is possible to see the prominences. Also the darkened sky is lightened by the corona, which may extend for more than a million miles from the sun's surface. Then a sliver of light reappears and the eclipse is over.

Fig. 3.13 Surveyor I self-portrait was one of 144 television pictures taken by the soft-lander spacecraft during its first day of operation on the lunar surface. Disk-shaped object in upper left is one of Surveyor's three feet. Attached members are parts of the landing leg. Beyond the foot is an area where the foot disturbed the lunar surface, apparently making an indentation with a pushed-up ridge of granular material around it. Long white object is one of the spacecraft's two omnidirectional antenna booms. Large, circular, two-tone object at bottom left, with fittings mounted above, is helium container. [Courtesy of Jet Propulsion Laboratory, NASA.]

As previously mentioned, the distance from the earth to the moon varies so that the umbra of the moon does not always reach the earth. In this case, an observer directly under the tip of the dark cone will see a thin ring of light surrounding the moon, the thin ring of light of the annular eclipse. This has a diameter about 30 miles wider than a total eclipse. Surrounding this area is a partial eclipse about 4000 to 6000 miles wide.

Eclipses can be predicted quite accurately for some time into the future. This is accomplished as a result of a detailed knowledge regarding the motions of the moon and the sun relative to the earth. The last eclipse took place on November 12, 1966, viewed from central South America and South Africa. Predictions for eclipses in the near future are:

November 2, 1967	Sandwich Islands and the Weddell Sea
September 22, 1968	Arctic and Central Asia
March 7, 1970	Florida and offshore Atlantic Coast

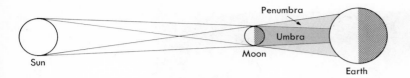

Fig. 3.14 An eclipse of the sun.

Mars. This, the fourth planet from the sun, was named after the Greek god of war. The Red Planet, as Mars is sometimes called, is a favorite with fiction writers. It has received more publicity as a supporter of life than any other planet, and consequently has been the focus of many science-fiction "men-from-Mars" stories. An incident which occurred in 1938 shows the extent of these ideas. A radio drama included a realistic account, in the form of a newscast, of a landing by Martian invaders in New Jersey. This caused the switchboards of radio stations, newspapers, and police departments to be flooded with telephone calls from people who believed such an invasion was actually taking place.

The basis for believing that intelligent life exists on Mars stems from the discovery and description of "canals" on Mars by Giovanni Schiaparelli in 1877. Lines on the surface of Mars appeared to be arranged in an organized fashion, giving credence to the theory that a civilization existed on Mars. Other astronomers have also seen the markings, but some have denied their existence. The Lowell Observatory in Arizona was organized in 1900 for the purpose of viewing and studying these lines.

Mars, during a favorable opposition, comes as close as 34 million miles, second closest of any of the planets to the earth. Since Mars has a thin atmosphere it is possible to observe surface features and determine many physical characteristics of this planet. Figures 3.15 and 3.16 show details of the Martian surface.

The planet revolves around the sun in 687 days and rotates on its axis in 24 hours, 37 minutes, and 22.67 seconds. Its diameter is 4200 miles or about half that of the earth. For this reason its mass is smaller and so is its gravitational attraction. Consequently some of the gases in the atmosphere have been permitted to escape, so that a much rarer atmosphere exists there than on earth. The major constituent of the Martian atmosphere is nitrogen, which is thought to make up about 96% of the total. Less than 1% is oxygen. Water vapor is only about 0.1% of the amount found in the atmosphere of the earth. Viewing of the surface is sometimes obscured by clouds thought to be vapor in the form of cirrus clouds as on earth. The haze disappears when the air of the planet is warmer and appears when the air is colder. In addition to this haze, there are clouds of yellow dust from dust storms which appear periodically, adding to the indistinctness of the surface.

The reddish or orange color of the planet is due to the surface material which covers about three-fifths of the surface. This material appears on the dry desert area of the planet and seems to be the source of the dust storms.

At each of the polar areas there is a polar cap which builds up and recedes as the seasons change. With the shrinking of the polar cap the areas close to it darken and the coloration gradually spreads toward the equator. These darker areas become more distinct and take on a greenish gray color. As the warm season progresses the color fades, giving much the same effect that could be expected if this material were vegetation.

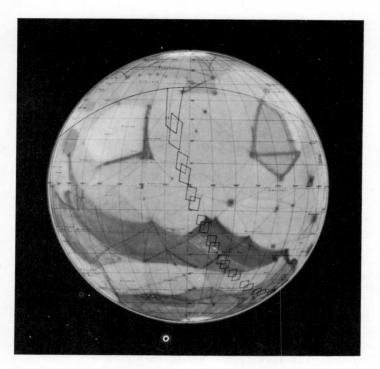

Fig. 3.15 Pictorial representation of Mars. [Prepared by Army Map Service, Corps of Engineers, U.S. Army.]

The type of vegetation that may exist on Mars is open to speculation. Studies of reflected light from these areas appear to rule out seed plants like those found on the earth. The plant types appear to be similar to our lichen and mosses. The growth of these plants must be as dense and extensive as a forested area on earth to be visible at this distance. A 30% cover on earth appears very sparse even at a close distance, and a cover of lichens and mosses appears as no cover at all. The vegetation, if such it is, may be like none seen on earth, growing very rapidly and very tall and being extremely efficient in its use of moisture.

Climatic conditions, with respect to the occurrence of seasons, are similar to those on the earth, but there the resemblance stops. Because Mars is much farther away from the sun than is the earth, it has a more vigorous climate. Surface temperatures in the "tropics" of Mars range from above freezing to 60°F, but generally temperatures are about 80°F to 100°F below the temperatures in comparable areas of the earth. It has been suggested that climatic conditions on Mars would be approached if the bleakest area of the Sahara desert were raised to an elevation of 60,000 feet.

Mars has two satellites, discovered in 1877, Phobos (fear) and Deimos (panic). Neither one is very large, not exceeding 10 miles in diameter, so they are difficult to see except under favorable conditions and with large telescopes. These are the smallest

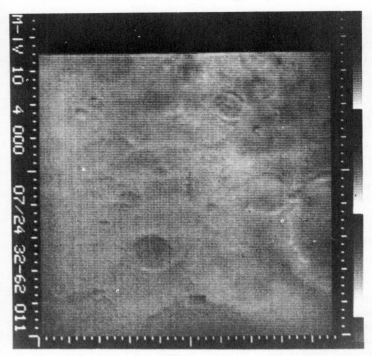

Fig. 3.16 The region covered represents an area of 170 miles by 160 miles, covered by patch, in that portion of Mars known as Atlantis on Mare Sirenum (see Fig. 3.15). Photo taken July 14, 1965, from an altitude of 8000 miles. [Courtesy of Jet Propulsion Laboratory, NASA.]

known satellites of any planet in the solar system. Phobos, the inner satellite, is 3700 miles from the surface and revolves around Mars in 7 hours, 39 minutes or about 3 times a day. The outer moon, Deimos, is 12,500 miles from Mars and revolves around the planet in 30 hours, 18 minutes. It is smaller than the inner satellite and so easily seen.

More than 100 years before their discovery, Voltaire made mention of two moons of Mars in a story, "Micromegas." During the same period Swift's Gulliver, in reporting on the achievements of the Laputans, refers to their observation of two Martian moons:

> *... whereof the innermost is distant from the center of the planet exactly three of his diameters and the outermost five; the former revolves in the space of ten hours and the latter in twenty-one and one-half hours.*

Jupiter. Jupiter is more than five times more distant than the earth from the sun, and revolves once around the sun in just under 12 years. Viewed through a telescope, Jupiter exhibits a variety of changing detail. It has a yellow background upon which a series of brown bands appear parallel to the equator. The period of rotation at the equator of

9 hours and 50 minutes indicates a speed of almost 30,000 miles an hour. The speed of rotation is not uniform for all latitudes, being somewhat lower nearer the polar areas. This would indicate that the atmosphere of Jupiter is of great depth. Because of the depth of atmosphere and the speed of rotation, the equator bulges to a diameter greater than the polar diameter by about 5700 miles. In addition to the banding there are also a number of dark markings on the surface which appear and disappear. One of these markings of considerable size has persisted for over a century. It is referred to as the "great red spot," is elliptical in shape, and is about 30,000 miles long by 7000 miles wide.

Knowledge of Jupiter's atmosphere is rather limited, but the available data are sufficient to indicate an extremely unfriendly environment. Extremely low temperatures would preclude the presence of water vapor. Methane, ammonia, and hydrogen make up the bulk of Jupiter's atmosphere. Much of the ammonia is in crystal form, because temperatures are below $-108°F$, the point at which ammonia solidifies.

Little is known of the surface of Jupiter because it is obscured by thousands of miles of atmosphere. At present, hydrogen in solid form is thought to make up the bulk of the hard core of Jupiter.

Jupiter is the planet with the greatest number of satellites, twelve being known at the present time. Only those first discovered by Galileo in 1610 were named and also numbered in order of their distance from the planet. For 280 years no new discoveries were made, but since 1892 eight additional satellites have been found. These have been given only a Roman numeral designation signifying the order of their discovery.

The four Galilean satellites are quite large; Io, for example, 2000 miles in diameter and Europa, 1800 miles in diameter, are both comparable with the moon, which is 2160 miles in diameter. Ganymede and Callisto are among the largest satellites in the solar system, being almost as large as the planet Mercury. Europa and Ganymede are of interest because they appear to be covered by snow. Except for comparatively lower temperatures, these may be much like the polar regions of the earth. Thus far no evidence exists to show there is an atmosphere on any of the satellites. The inner group comprises these four and V. Satellite V is much smaller than the other four and orbits around the planet at much faster pace than any of the other satellites in the solar system, moving at about 1000 miles a minute. The common feature of these five satellites is their nearly circular orbit on the equatorial plane of Jupiter.

The second group includes satellites VI, VII, and X. These orbit Jupiter at a distance of slightly more than 7 million miles approximately every 260 days. The paths of their orbits are sufficiently eccentric and at varying angles from the equatorial plane, so that the satellites are not in danger of collision. These three, together with the outer four satellites, are so faint that the light reflected from them can be compared to the light from a candle viewed from a distance of 3000 miles. The outer four satellites include XII, XI, VIII, and IX at a distance of more than 14 million miles from Jupiter and make one circuit of the planet in slightly more than two years. This group revolves around Jupiter from east to west in the opposite direction from the other satellites. These satellites are so far from the planet that its gravitational influence is weak and their orbits are influenced to some extent by the sun.

Knowledge based on observation of the Galilean satellites was an important factor in the discovery of the finite nature of the speed of light. Until Olaus Roemer discovered otherwise in 1676 it had been the general feeling that light could be seen instantaneously in any part of the universe. He measured the period of revolution of the Galilean moons, particularly Io, and found a difference depending on whether the earth was moving toward or away from Jupiter. Making exact measurements for the period of Io, he found that this satellite required 42 hours, 27 minutes, and 33 seconds to make one revolution. This time could readily be determined to the second. He found that as the earth moved away from Jupiter, the period of revolution of Io was 14 seconds longer. In three-months' time, the predicted location of Io was more than 10 minutes off. From this information, Roemer was able to calculate the speed of light at a little over 140,000 miles per second. The speed of light, since that time, has been measured many times by other methods; the accepted velocity is now about 186,000 miles per second.

Saturn. Saturn, noted for its rings, was the most distant planet known to early astronomers. It is nearly twice as far from the sun as Jupiter; it is second largest in the solar system; and it requires 29.5 years to revolve once around the sun.

Atmospheric conditions on Saturn are similar to those on Jupiter except that ammonia is less concentrated, because of lower temperature, and methane is stronger. Because of the deep, dense atmosphere, the main body of the planet is not visible but is thought to be made up mainly of hydrogen in solid form as is Jupiter's.

The rings around Saturn are a unique feature of this planet. These are three concentric rings in the equatorial plane. The inner ring (crepe ring) is visible only with a large telescope and is contiguous to the middle ring (bright ring). This in turn is separated from the outer ring by a distance of about 3000 miles, called Cassini's gap after its discoverer. The rings extend out to a distance of 85,000 miles from the center of Saturn, and have a thickness of from 10 to 20 miles.

Saturn's rings are made up of a multitude of discrete sand-sized particles revolving around the planet in a nearly circular orbit in the direction of Saturn's rotation. According to Roche's theorem, for a large solid body (or solid ring) to form it has to be at a distance of at least 2.44 times the planetary radius from the center of the planet. The rings are within this radius and are stable only because they are made up of separate particles. These particles are thought to be ice.

In addition to the rings and outside Roche's limits, Saturn also has ten known satellites. The largest of these is Titan, 2850 miles in diameter, the only satellite in the solar system known to have an atmosphere, probably methane. Eight of the moons are within 1 million miles of Saturn, one is a little more than 2 million miles from Saturn, and Phoebe, the smallest, is over 8 million miles from Saturn. Phoebe revolves from east to west as do Jupiter's outer moons.

Uranus. All the planets previously discussed were known to ancient astronomers, since they are readily visible to the naked eye. Uranus has the distinction of being the first planet discovered after the invention of the telescope. It is faintly visible to the naked eye, and records show that it had been sighted a number of times previously but was always mistaken for a star. In 1781 William Herschel, a musician and amateur astronomer, saw a disk-shaped object he first mistook for a comet. After observing this new body for several months, he realized that this was, indeed, a new planet since it was a well-defined orb, not hazy like a comet, and since the orbit was much more circular than the normal long elliptical orbit followed by a comet. The name, Uranus, for the Greek god of the heavens, was suggested by Bode.

An orbit for this new planet could not be determined from the previous sighting. New data had to be accumulated for this purpose. By 1821 an orbit had been calculated, but in a few years Uranus began to wander off course, indicating the presence of still another unseen planet. In 20 years' time, Uranus deviated from its calculated orbit by two minutes of arc, an error too large to be observational.

Uranus appears greenish in color and has banded markings similar to those of Jupiter and Saturn. The atmosphere is primarily methane in a gaseous form with little or no ammonia present because of the low temperature. No surface markings are visible, so the period of rotation of 10 hours and 45 minutes had to be determined by spectroscopic analysis, which is less accurate than visual observation.

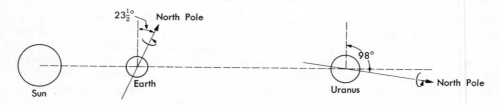

Fig. 3.17 The axial inclination of Uranus from the perpendicular to the ecliptic plane is 98°.

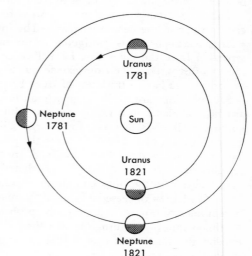

Fig. 3.18 Neptune pulls Uranus ahead of its predicted position for 40 years.

An unusual feature of Uranus is that the axis of rotation is almost horizontal to the ecliptic plane (Fig. 3.17), giving the planet the appearance of rolling along in its orbit. The north pole from which the direction of rotation would appear to be counter-clockwise is actually inclined 98° from the perpendicular to the ecliptic plane. This orientation is used so that Uranus' rotation conforms to that of the other planets in the solar system. If the pole which actually points in a northerly direction were used for designating direction of rotation, Uranus would rotate in a clockwise direction, opposite to that of other planets.

Uranus has five known satellites in an equatorial orbit. The direction of revolution would be counterclockwise if viewed from the Uranian north pole. These satellites are a few hundred miles in diameter with the exception of Titania which is about 1000 miles in diameter.

Neptune.   While Uranus has the distinction of being the first planet discovered with the telescope, Neptune is equally notable for having its existence predicted on the basis of deviations noted in the orbit of Uranus. The manner in which this occurred is shown in Fig. 3.18. Uranus, on an inner orbit from Neptune, is attracted by Neptune's mass and is speeded up as it moves around in its orbit. This is why Uranus arrived at its 1821 location slightly before schedule. Then Neptune falls behind Uranus, therefore slowing Uranus and permitting it to arrive at its starting point on schedule.

Knowledge of the possibility of such a situation led John Adams, an undergraduate student at Cambridge, to calculate the probable location of the unknown planet. In 1845 he communicated his solution to Sir George Airy, the Astronomer Royal, who in turn wrote to Adams requesting further information on the orbit of Uranus. Adams never bothered to answer, so there the matter rested.

Unaware of all this, a French mathematician, Urbain Leverrier, also calculated the position of a planet on the basis of Uranus' orbital deviation. He wrote to Johann Galle at the Berlin Observatory in 1846, suggesting that Galle examine a particular region of the sky. On the basis of Leverrier's data, Galle discovered the planet that same evening, about one degree from Leverrier's predicted position.

An Englishman, a Frenchman, and a German were involved in the discovery of Neptune. Pride being what it is, the debate that followed as to who should be credited with the discovery inevitably followed nationalistic lines. The participants themselves never entered the controversy but instead congratulated each other, and eventually all were credited with the part they had played.

Because of its extreme distance from the earth, little is known about Neptune. It is sometimes referred to as "Uranus' twin" because of their similarity with respect to size, temperature, and atmospheric conditions. It has not yet completed one revolution of its orbit since its discovery, and will not complete one revolution until 2011 A.D.

Neptune has two known satellites. Triton, the larger of the two and closest to the primary, revolves in an east to west direction. The second satellite, Nereid, has an eccentric orbit such that it is closest at less than one million miles and farthest away at more than six million miles. It revolves around the planet in the normal manner from west to east in just about one year.

Pluto.   This mysterious planet is farthest from the sun of the known planets, being at an average distance of 3.67 billion miles, or 39.5 *AU*. The discovery of Pluto was not accidental. Its presence was surmised early in the twentieth century as a result of small unaccountable orbital deviations of Uranus and Neptune. Percival Lowell, founder of the Lowell Observatory in Arizona, sought the hidden planet from 1906 until his death in 1916. The search was discontinued until 1929 when a new photographic telescope was installed at the Lowell Observatory. A young astronomer, C. W. Tombaugh, using this equipment, continued Lowell's search and in March 1930 announced the presence of the ninth planet. The name Pluto was suggested by a young girl from England and was considered entirely appropriate since the first two letters of the name were the initials of Percival Lowell. In addition, Pluto was the Greek god of the nether regions, reminiscent of the dark reaches of space where the new planet was found.

It has been suggested that Pluto originally was a satellite of Neptune, which had escaped into an orbit of its own. This reasoning is based in part on Pluto's unusual orbit which at aphelion is 1.8 billion miles beyond Neptune's orbit, but at perihelion comes inside Neptune's orbit by 35 million miles. The possibility of a collision is negligible provided the planets stay in their existing orbits. Under present conditions their closest approach is about 240 million miles.

Little is known about the surface features of Pluto. Temperatures go below −400°F, which means most gases, if present, are in liquid or solid form. The surface is probably covered with a gritty snowlike material, and the atmosphere would be extremely rare, if it existed at all.

After the discovery of Pluto, some astronomers questioned whether so small a planet (3600 miles in diameter) could be responsible for influencing such large planets as Uranus and Neptune. Percival Lowell, in his *Memoir on a Trans-Neptunian Planet,* indicated that the "Planet X" had a mass seven times that of the earth and was at a mean distance of 43 AU from the sun. A planet with the mass and diameter ascribed to Pluto would be an extremely dense body, much more dense than anything experienced on the earth. At present, the mass of Pluto is thought to be about equal to that of the earth, but even this gives Pluto a density of approximately 50 gm/cm^3. Densities of this magnitude are unknown in the solar system but are a property of certain dying stars known as white dwarfs. These will be discussed in a later chapter.

The reason for this phenomenon is at present a matter of speculation. One cause for the high apparent density may lie in the fact that the true diameter of Pluto is not known. What is measured as the diameter of the planet may be only a highlight of the light reflected from the planet. Pluto is a dark sphere in a distant dark portion of the solar system, receiving only a very small amount of light from the sun. Only a portion of the total sphere may be visible to observers on the earth.

If Pluto's true diameter is about 3600 miles, then the cause for its high apparent density may be the existence of an undetected tenth planet in space beyond Pluto. The influence of this tenth planet, combined with that of Pluto, could explain the unaccountably high densities and orbital deviations of Uranus and Neptune.

A third explanation which has been suggested is that Pluto is not a planet after all, but rather a dead star, a former small companion of the sun which, because of its small size, expired millions of years ago. Known dead stars have extremely high densities as a result of the collapse of the matter from which they are made. If the theories now held as to how stars evolve are true, however, this explanation has little validity.

Comets.   About five to ten comets appear each year but are usually so faint that they are invisible to the unaided eye. However, the chance of seeing a large one during one's lifetime is good since Halley's Comet, last reported in 1910, reappears every 76 years. Comets have for centuries been cause for concern, as harbingers of disasters. Records of their appearances go back 2500 years, with Halley's Comet traced as far back as 240 B.C.

The head of a comet is a large body called the *coma,* the center of which has a bright nucleus. The size of the coma varies depending on how close the comet is to the sun. When Halley's Comet was 300 million miles from the sun, the diameter of the coma was about 14,000 miles. At perihelion it swelled to 120,000 miles and, when last seen, had shrunk to 30,000 miles.

From the coma streams a long filmy tail. The tail is dimmer than the coma and it is difficult to determine where one ends and the other begins. Most comets do not have tails which are characteristic of only large comets. Usually the tails are formed at distances of less than 1.5 AU from the sun and may attain lengths of 1 to 2 AU.

Material in the nucleus is thought to include methane (CH_4), ammonia (NH_3), carbon dioxide (CO_2), and water. The coma and the tail are formed from compounds resulting from the chemical disruption of the materials in the nucleus by action of unfiltered, solar, ultraviolet radiation. The light emitted from the tail is caused by the absorption of certain rays from the sun by particles of the comet, and their immediate re-emission.

Comets are not visitors from outer space. They are members of the solar system and, therefore, may have reasonably predictable orbits. Halley's Comet moves in an extremely elliptical orbit from close to the sun at perihelion to beyond Neptune's orbit at aphelion. As the comet approaches the sun, the tail becomes more prominent. The tail is repelled by the light of the sun so that it is pointed away from the sun when the comet swings around and reverses its orbit. As the comet leaves the influence of the sun, the tail diminishes in size and eventually disappears.

The repulsion of a comet's tail appears to be the result of pressure from the light of the sun. This pressure has been demonstrated to be extremely small but measurable. It is equivalent to a pressure of two pounds exerted over an area of one square mile of the earth's surface.

The tail of Halley's Comet and all other comets is so tenuous that stars can be seen through it without appreciable loss of brightness. Actually, the earth has passed through it without apparent effect.

Comets do not last indefinitely; they eventually dissipate their material. It is estimated that the average life of a comet is about 70 passages around the sun. The question can then be raised, Where does the current supply of comets come from? From a statistical study of known comets making frequent orbits around the sun, there is reason to believe that there may be as many as 100 billion comets in a *comet cloud* revolving about the sun in an orbit extending out to a distance of 150,000 AU or more. These make very infrequent visits but, when doing so, may be "captured" by Jupiter or one of the other large planets. These captured comets replace the current short-period comets as they dissipate, thereby maintaining a more or less steady population of comets making regular appearances.

Meteors, Meteoroids, and Meteorites.   The bright streak frequently seen in the night sky and referred to as a meteor or "shooting star" is caused by a meteoroid or solid particle from space entering the atmosphere of the earth. On the average about five to ten meteors an hour may be visible on a clear night, each lasting for about half a second. The frequency is greater after midnight, when the side of the earth that is turned away from the sun faces into the stream of particles. An estimated 100 million visible meteoroids fall to earth each day. Many more invisible meteoroids also land on the surface of the earth, being so small that they keep relatively cool by radiating heat fast enough to prevent its accumulation. These may be as small as one-thousandth of an inch or less in diameter and are called micrometeors. Many, however, are large enough to survive the flight through the atmosphere and not be completely burned up. These meteorites, as they are called, may be found on the ground.

Most meteoroids enter the atmosphere, become visible at a height of 55 to 75 miles above the surface, and burn up and disappear between altitudes of 45 and 60 miles. Speed of entry has been measured quite accurately and found to range from 7 to 45 miles per second.

At these speeds the particle becomes heated to incandescence. However, the light that is seen is not the result of this heat, since a particle the size of a grain of sand at a distance of 50 miles would hardly be visible. It is believed that gases in the path traveled by the meteoroid are ionized. The recombination of ions into atoms in this cylinder of air results in the release of energy in the form of light which is visible. The action is similar to that occurring in a neon sign, where light is emitted without the generation of a great deal of heat.

Meteoroids go around the sun in highly eccentric orbits similar to those of comets. Consequently, it has been presumed that meteoroids may be of cometary origin. Most meteoroids are of a sporadic nature, appearing at random times and from random directions. Some appear in a more organized pattern as meteor showers. The particles in these showers enter the atmosphere of the earth along parallel paths, but because of the perspective of distance, the meteor trails appear to come from a common point. Most of the showers are named after constellations which are the background for the apparent center of the meteor shower. For example, Leonids appear to come from the constellation Leo and Draconids from Draco. The showers occur when the earth encounters a meteor swarm or a meteor stream.

A meteor swarm, sometimes described as a "flying gravel pile," is a mass of meteoric particles orbiting the sun as a group. The particles are not very close, averaging about 1 particle per 2 million cubic miles. The meteoroids of a stream are distributed over the entire orbit. The diameters of the swarms or streams vary from 500,000 miles to 50 million miles and their orbits reach far out into the solar system.

Many millions of meteoroids enter the atmosphere of the earth each day but very few reach the surface as sizable meteorites. The largest single-particle meteorite thus far discovered was found in Northern Greenland by the explorer R. E. Peary and weighed 34 tons. Larger meteorites have resulted in the formation of craters, of which the Barringer crater in Northeast Arizona is an example. The crater measures 4200 feet in diameter and is 570 feet deep. The depth is measured from the rim which is about 135 feet above the surrounding terrain. The meteorite responsible for the crater is estimated to have been about 200 feet in diameter and to have weighed about one million tons. The entire mass apparently exploded on contact since the largest particle so far located weighs less than one ton. Another such crater, discovered in 1950 in northeastern Canada, has a diameter 2½ times that of the Barringer Crater. Other craters have been found in Australia and in Siberia.

Meteorites are generally classified in three categories. The stony types, *aerolites,* are composed mainly of silicates, of which the iron-magnesium silicates are the most common. These materials are similar to the olivine and pyroxene found on earth. *Siderites* are made up essentially of an iron-nickel alloy in which the average proportion of iron is about 90%. The *siderolites* are made up of iron-nickel and silicates in about equal parts. The silicate is usually olivine.

Asteroids.   The asteroids, also known as minor planets or planetoids, are the thousands of small bodies which revolve around the sun mainly between the orbits of Mars and Jupiter. The direction of rotation is west to east in common with most other bodies in the solar system, and the period of revolution ranges from 3½ years for some asteroids to 6 years for others. As a result of the prediction made from Bode's Law, Ceres was discovered in 1801. It is the largest of the asteroids, having a diameter of 480 miles.

Pallas, discovered in 1802, is 304 miles in diameter; Juno, 1804, 120 miles in diameter; and Vesta, 1807, 240 miles in diameter. These are the only asteroids for which the diameters have been measured. Other diameters are estimated from their brightness, on the assumption that all reflect as much light as the four largest asteroids. Estimates made by this method indicate that about 500 asteroids have diameters of more than 30 miles. Most of the asteroids discovered recently have been from 5 to 20 miles in diameter.

For a time after the discovery of Ceres, asteroids were eagerly sought after, but in recent years little interest has been exhibited in these bodies. New discoveries have been mostly accidental and have been made during the process of photographing some other object. Only asteroids with orbits close to the earth have been watched with any interest.

Since 1932 several have been discovered quite close to the earth. Apollo, discovered in 1932, had its perihelion inside the orbit of Venus and passed within 3 million miles of the earth. Adonis, discovered in 1936, passed within 1 million miles of the orbits of Venus, Earth and Mars. In 1937 Hermes was discovered, passing within 600,000 miles of the earth. All these asteroids were quite small, being only about one mile in diameter. Icarus, 1949, approaches closest to the sun of any known body. At perihelion it is about 17 million miles from the sun. The asteroid which goes farthest from the sun is Hidalgo, whose orbit reaches out almost to Saturn.

At present about 1600 asteroids are named or numbered. It is estimated that about 44,000 are large enough to reflect sufficient light to be photographed by the 100-inch telescope when they are nearest the earth. Many of the smaller asteroids fluctuate in brightness periodically. This fluctuation may be due to the irregular shape of the body. Eros, for example, alternates bright and dim every 70 minutes. It is thought to be shaped like a brick, about 15 miles in length and 5 miles in width and thickness. If this premise is correct, rotation on its axis would cause large and small faces to be turned toward the earth alternately, resulting in changes in brightness. The irregular shape of asteroids suggests that they may be fragments resulting from the collision of larger bodies. Many of the fragments could have been thrown into orbits which do not conform to the average orbits of the asteroids and may have collided with earth as meteorites.

3.5   SUMMARY

The solar system consists of the sun, which contains 99% of the mass of the solar system, the planets and their satellites, and various other smaller bodies such as comets, meteoroids, and asteroids. Mercury, Venus, Mars, Jupiter, and Saturn are visible to the unaided eye and were seen by ancient astronomers. Uranus, Neptune, and Pluto have been discovered since the invention of the telescope and cannot be seen without such an instrument.

Despite the great distances involved a surprising amount of information has been gathered on the physical characteristics of the planets and some of the other members of the solar system. The sun is the sole source of energy, energy produced by the conversion of hydrogen to helium. All other bodies in the solar system are visible only because of the light they reflect. None produce energy in the same manner as does the sun.

Comets are thought to occur as a "cloud" around the solar system. In following extremely elliptical orbits they occasionally come close to the sun and may be influenced by one of the larger planets, causing the comet to take up a regular orbit around the sun. During these passages around the sun the comet constantly loses material. Eventually the comet disappears, but the material continues to orbit as meteoroids. When the earth occasionally passes through such a stream or swarm of these meteoroids, "shooting stars" are visible in the sky and occasionally a meteorite lands on the earth's surface. Asteroids travel in an orbit between Mars and Jupiter. These are small bodies (the largest is only 480 miles in diameter) which may be the debris of a planet that broke up, or material which never formed a planet.

SUGGESTED READINGS

Jet Propulsion Laboratory Staff, *Mariner Mission to Venus.* New York: McGraw-Hill, 1963.

KUIPER, G. P., ed., *Planets and Satellites.* Chicago: University of Chicago Press, 1961.

MENZEL, D. H., *Our Sun,* rev. ed. Cambridge, Mass.: Harvard University Press, 1959.

SHAPLEY, H., ed., *Source Book in Astronomy 1900–1950.* Cambridge, Mass.: Harvard University Press, 1960.

UREY, H. C., *The Planets, Their Origin and Development.* New Haven, Conn.: Yale University Press, 1952.

WATSON, F. G., *Between the Planets,* rev. ed. Cambridge, Mass.: Harvard University Press, 1956.

WHIPPLE, F. L., *Earth, Moon and Planets.* Cambridge, Mass.: Harvard University Press, 1963.

CHAPTER 4

STARS

The solar system consists of the planets with their satellites, asteroids, and other miscellaneous particles, all dominated by the sun. From the earth, at night, it is possible to see hundreds of stars which are like the sun rather than the earth, because these stars are generating energy. The difference we find between them and the sun is due chiefly to their distance from the earth. All that is known about the stars has been learned by studying the light which is gathered and analyzed by means of telescope and spectroscope. Yet a great deal has been learned about individual stars which permits a characterization of the entire stellar population.

4.1 STELLAR DISTANCE

One of the more important problems that required solution was the determination of distance, for it is on the basis of distance that the determination of other physical properties of stars depends. The ancient Greeks, while they understood the principle of parallax, were unable to detect the parallactic displacement of stars with the instruments available to them. This is not surprising when it is realized that the angle of parallax of the nearest star is less than 1 second of arc using the earth's orbital diameter (186 million miles) as a base. The first serious effort to detect and measure parallax was made by William Herschel in the eighteenth century. He attempted to accomplish this by studying the relative movement of pairs of stars seen in his telescope. Although he was unable to detect parallax, he did discover the existence of many binary (double) stars which exerted a mutual attraction on each other and revolved around a common center of gravity.

It was not until 1838 that a German astronomer, F. W. Bessel, made the first reliable measurement of stellar distance. He chose 61 Cygni, a star just visible to the unaided eye which had previously been seen to move through space at an angular distance of 5 seconds of arc a year. Because of this angular motion, he deduced that the star was relatively close to the earth.

The method of measuring parallax is similar to the method of triangulation used by surveyors to find the distance to some point not easily accessible (Fig. 4.1). To find the distance from A to C, a line AB is laid out and carefully measured. Angle A and angle B can be determined, and from this information, the distance AC can be calculated.

A similar technique is used for calculating stellar distance. The diameter of the earth's orbit is used as a baseline (Fig. 4.2), and the position of the star is noted at six-month intervals against the background of more distant stars that do not change their relative position. The displacement is a measure of the parallax. By common consent of astron-

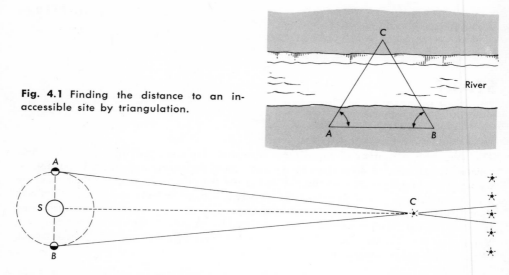

Fig. 4.1 Finding the distance to an inaccessible site by triangulation.

Fig. 4.2 Triangulation is used to find the distance to a nearby star. To obtain the parallactic angle at C, measurements are made when the earth is at A and six months later when it is at B.

omers, the earth's orbital radius is used as the baseline, and therefore angle *SCB* is known as the parallax. With this information it is possible to calculate *SC*. While this represents the distance from the star to the sun, it can also be used as the distance from the star to the earth because in measuring stellar distances, the earth's orbital radius is insignificant.

The measurement of the extremely small angles involved (0.76 second of arc for the nearest star) is tedious and requires great patience. Recordings must be made at six-month intervals over several years in order to obtain a correct set of measurements. This extended period of observation is necessary because the star being studied is in motion and a correction for this motion must be made. Furthermore the solar system is in motion and the observer's position changes, necessitating a corresponding correction. Even refraction of light by the atmosphere must be reckoned with, as well as the peculiarities of the instrument being used. Bessel considered these factors in his calculation and measured the angular parallax of 61 Cygni as slightly under 0.3 second of arc. From this he determined the distance to 61 Cygni as approximately 696,000 AU.

It can be seen that distances to the stars are great and the units of measurement used within the confines of the solar system become too cumbersome for stellar distances. For this reason, a simple unit of measure, easily definable, is necessary. The light-year fits these requirements and is defined as the distance traveled in one year by a light beam which we know has a velocity of 186,000 miles per second. This makes the distance from 61 Cygni to the earth 11 light-years, a much easier quantity to handle and remember. Another unit of measure used for stellar distances is the parsec. The *parsec* is the distance to a point in space such that the angle of parallax is equal to 1 second of arc. This distance is equal to 3.26 light-years or 206,265 AU. This would make the distance to 61 Cygni about 3.4 parsecs. A simple formula gives the relationship between parallax and distance:

$$D \text{ (parsec)} = \frac{1}{p \text{ (seconds of arc)}} \cdot$$

After Bessel reported his first stellar distance, scarcely fifty more were determined in the next fifty years. When photography was introduced as an astronomical technique, this endeavor was greatly speeded up so that several thousand stellar distances have now been determined by parallactic displacement. Because of the very small angular measurements, the use of parallax is limited to measuring the distance to stars which are relatively close to the earth. For all practical purposes, the point where error limits the use of parallax for measuring stellar distances is at about 100 parsecs. Beyond this point, distances are measured by indirect means.

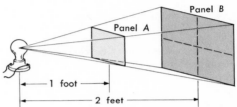

Fig. 4.3 Panel A is one-half the distance from the light source that panel B is and receives four times the light energy.

Several methods are available for determining stellar distances indirectly and all are dependent on the apparent brightness of the light coming from a star. Apparent brightness is a function of the amount of light coming from the source and the distance the source is from the observer. The relationship is such that at double the distance, the light is only one-fourth as bright, while at half the distance, the light is four times as bright. In Fig. 4.3 a beam of light striking a screen one square foot in area at one foot from the source would be four times as bright as the same beam of light striking a screen two feet from the source. The same amount of light energy is covering four times the area. This fact provides a simple law which states that the apparent brightness of a light source is inversely proportional to the square of the distance from the source or, mathematically,

$$L = \frac{1}{d^2},$$

where L is the apparent brightness or luminosity, and d is the distance. This method involves having some knowledge of the properties of stars. As will be shown later, stars may be categorized into groups on the basis of similar properties. Thus a star whose distance from the earth has been established by measuring its parallax may be similar to a very distant star. The comparative luminosities can be measured photoelectrically and from this information it is possible to calculate the distance of the more distant star with a satisfactory degree of accuracy. A star measured to be one-fourth as bright as a similar star can be regarded as being twice the distance from the observer.

A group of stars very useful for indirectly determining distances are the pulsating stars known as the Cepheids. These vary in brightness at regular intervals, a discovery made by Henrietta Leavitt in 1908. It was found that the brightness of these stars is related to the length of the cycle (period) through which the brightness varies (Fig. 4.4). Cepheid stars having the same period have the same brightness, and the longer the period, the brighter the star. Therefore, from Cepheids of known distance, it is possible to determine the distance to Cepheids of similar period which are too far away to permit measurement by parallax.

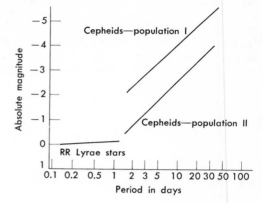

Fig. 4.4 Period-luminosity curve for Cepheid variable stars.

4.2 STELLAR MAGNITUDE

Hipparchus was the first astronomer to catalog the stars on the basis of brightness. He assigned numbers, ranging from 1 to 6, to about a thousand stars to indicate relative magnitude, with 1 for the approximately twenty very bright stars and 6 for those stars just barely visible. This system worked admirably until the invention of the telescope when many more stars were revealed, and numbers were added to include these new stars in the system. It can be seen that in this system the larger magnitude numbers apply to the fainter stars. Measurements made of the radiation of various stars revealed that stars of magnitude 1 were about 100 times brighter than stars of magnitude 6. This led in the nineteenth century to the adoption of a magnitude scale in which two stars having a difference in brightness of 100 differ by 5 magnitudes. This means that a star of the first magnitude is 100 times brighter than a star of the sixth magnitude. By the same token, a star of magnitude 8 is 100 times brighter than one of magnitude 13. The brightness ratio between two stars differing by 1 magnitude is the fifth root of 100, or 2.512. In other words, a star of the third magnitude is 2.512 times brighter than a star of the fourth magnitude. It can be seen from the foregoing that the magnitude of a star is not proportional to the brightness. Doubling the magnitude of a star does not result in a doubling of brightness. The difference in brightness between two stars may be found by raising 2.512 to a power equal to the difference in magnitude of the two stars. For example, star A of magnitude 4 is $(2.512)^3$ times brighter than star B of magnitude 7.

This system supplies the apparent magnitude of a star as seen by an observer on earth. A star may be extremely large and extremely bright but because of its great distance appear faint to an observer. On this type of scale, based on apparent magnitude, the sun is the brightest object in the sky; it is much brighter than stars of the first magnitude. This has brought about the necessity for using negative magnitudes. The

TABLE 4.1   PROPERTIES OF CERTAIN PROMINENT STARS

Name	Distance, parsecs	Apparent magnitude (mv) ‡	Absolute magnitude (Mv) ‡	Spectral class
Sun	——	−26.7	4.9	G2
*Alpha Centauri	1.3	0.0	4.4	G2
†Barnard's Star	1.8	9.5	13.2	M5
*Sirius	2.7	−1.4	1.5	A1
†61 Cygni	3.4	5.2	7.5	K6
*Procyon	3.5	0.3	2.6	F5
Altair	5.1	0.8	2.6	A7
Formalhaut	6.9	1.2	2.0	A3
Vega	8.0	0.0	0.5	A0
Arcturus	11.0	−0.1	−0.3	K2
Pollux	11.0	1.2	1.0	K0
*Castor	14.0	1.6	0.9	A1
*Capella	14.0	0.1	−0.6	G2
Aldebaran	16.0	0.9	−0.7	K5
Achernar	20.0	0.5	−3.0	B5
*Regulus	26.0	1.4	−0.6	B7
Canopus	30.0	−0.7	−4.0	F0
Bellatrix	40.0	1.6	−2.0	B2
*Spica	80.0	1.0	−2.0	B1
Betelgeuse	150.0	0.7	−5.5	M2
*Rigel	250.0	0.1	−6.8	B8
Deneb	430.0	1.3	−6.9	A2

* Multiple star systems
† Accompanied by dark companions
‡ The abbreviations mv and Mv stand for "magnitude visual." It is customary to use a lower-case "m" for apparent magnitude and an upper-case "M" for absolute magnitude.

sun, therefore, has an apparent magnitude of −26.7, and the moon, which is the second brightest object in the sky, has an apparent magnitude of −12.7. Next in order of brilliance is the planet Venus, with a magnitude of −4.2. The brightest star in the sky is Sirius (Alpha Canis Majoris) with an apparent magnitude of −1.4. Magnitudes of other stars may be found in Table 4.1.

Many times it is desirable to compare the brightness of several stars without the complicating factor of distance. For this purpose the concept of absolute magnitude has been introduced. Absolute magnitude is the magnitude a star would have if it were at a standard distance of 10 parsecs from the observer on earth. This means that stars at great distances would appear much brighter while stars that are relatively close would be dimmer. The sun with an apparent magnitude of −26.7 would have an absolute magnitude of 4.9 at the standard distance, becoming one of the fainter stars visible to the unaided eye. Absolute magnitude may be calculated from either of two formulas:

$$M = m + 5 + 5 \log p \qquad \text{or} \qquad M = m + 5 - 5 \log d,$$

where M and m are the absolute and the apparent magnitude, respectively, p is the parallax in seconds of arc, and d is the distance in parsecs. If the apparent magnitude and distances are known, absolute magnitude may be determined.

Magnitude determined by eye is somewhat different from magnitude obtained from a photographic plate, because the reaction of the photographic emulsion is different from that of the retina of the eye. The difference between these two values for a given star results in a quality called the *color index* of a star. There exists a relationship between the color index and temperature which makes the visual apparent magnitude and photographic apparent magnitude of value in determining the surface temperatures of distant stars. The same technique may be applied when one uses absolute magnitudes.

4.3   STELLAR TEMPERATURES

Several methods of measuring the temperature of distant bodies have been presented. The thermocouple (Section 2.4) has been found to be most useful in measuring energy in the infrared part of the spectrum. The spectroscopic determination of the most intense wavelength of radiation can be used to calculate temperature by the application of Wien's law (Section 2.6), while the use of visual and photographic magnitudes (Section 4.2) has provided an indirect means of temperature measurement. By combining and comparing data obtained by the several methods, values for temperatures of many stars have been obtained. Temperatures of some representative stars are given in Table 4.2.

4.4   STELLAR DIAMETERS

The diameter of the sun can be readily calculated because its angular diameter and distance can easily be measured. Stars, on the other hand, appear as pinpoints of light in even the most powerful telescopes because of the great distances involved. Several ingenious methods of measuring stellar diameters have been devised, however, so that the sizes of many stars are now known. A. A. Michelson made the first such determination in 1920, using the 100-inch telescope on Mount Wilson. He made use of a device called an *interferometer* to measure the angular diameter of some of the nearer stars. Michelson found the angular diameter of Betelgeuse to be 0.047 second of arc, and the parallax 0.018 second of arc. Having determined the distance, he then computed the diameter to be 250 million miles. This method has been used for fewer than twenty of the nearer stars, however, because of the cumbersome equipment required for more refined measurement. The data even for these few have been of great importance, nevertheless, since this has made it possible to verify the correctness of the diameters of stars calculated by indirect methods.

Diameter may also be determined if the luminosity and temperature of a star are known. The luminosity is dependent on the star's radiant energy which is a function of temperature, and on the size (diameter) of the stars. This relationship can be expressed by the following formula:

$$D = \left(\frac{5770}{T}\right)^2 \times \sqrt{L},$$

where D is the stellar diameter expressed in units of solar diameter, T is the absolute

TABLE 4.2   CHARACTERISTICS OF THE SPECTRAL CLASSES

Spectral class	Color	Temperature, °F	Principal characteristics	Representative Stars
O	Blue	> 45,000	Lines of ionized helium and other elements are present. Hydrogen lines are weak	10 Lacertae
B	Bluish-white	19,500–45,000	Stronger hydrogen lines than in Type O. Neutral helium and some ionized elements present	Achernar, Spica
A	White	13,000–19,500	Strong hydrogen lines. Ionized calcium, iron, magnesium, and others. No helium lines	Sirius
F	Yellow-white	10,500–13,000	Hydrogen lines weaker than in Type-A stars. Calcium lines are prominent along with some metals	Procyon
G	Yellow	8500–10,500	Strong calcium lines and metals are prominent. Hydrogen lines are weak	Sun
K	Yellow-orange	5800–8500	Lines of metals are dominant. Molecular TiO is present. Hydrogen very weak	Arcturus
M	Red	< 5800	Strong lines of metals and strong molecular bands of TiO	Betelgeuse
R	Yellow-orange	5800–8500	Same characteristics as Type-K star except molecular bands of carbon molecule are present	
N	Red	< 5800	Same characteristics as Type-M star except molecular bands of carbon molecule are present	
S	Red	< 5800	ZrO present instead of TiO as in Type-M star	

temperature (°Kelvin), and L is the star's luminosity. A star's luminosity is also expressed in solar units. Sirius will serve as an example to illustrate the diameter determination: Its temperature is 9800°K and its luminosity is 27 times that of the sun. The diameter of Sirius will then be

$$\left(\frac{5770}{9800}\right)^2 \times \sqrt{27} = 1.8 \text{ times the diameter of the sun.}$$

While this is an indirect method and subject to error, most stellar diameters are measured in this way, and for practical purposes the method is satisfactory.

4.5   STELLAR MASS AND DENSITY

The mass of a celestial body is difficult to measure unless it is possible to determine its gravitational effect on a nearby body. Within the solar system, the mass of planets can be found when there are satellites, but the problem becomes more complex with those planets which do not have satellites. Knowledge of stellar masses is, for the most part, based on information obtained from binary stars, where the effect of the components upon each other can be studied. While stars vary greatly in such properties as brightness and diameter, the range in mass compared with that of the sun is, for the most part, rather narrow. There are stars with a mass 100 times that of the sun, but these are extremely rare. The heaviest known star is HD 698 with a mass about 113 times that of the sun, while Luyten 726-8 has a mass of about 0.04 that of the sun. For the great majority of stars the mass is between 0.1 and about 5 times that of the sun.

Binary stars may be compared to the earth and the moon, where the system is made up of two bodies revolving around a common center of gravity. Visual binaries are those in which the two stars of the pair are distinguishable to an observer on earth.

The use of Newton's modification of Kepler's Third Law makes it possible to express the mass of a pair of binary stars in the following terms:

$$M + m = \frac{a^3}{p^2}$$

where M and m represent the mass of the separate components in terms of solar mass; a is the mean distance between the components in astronomical units; and p is the period in years necessary for the stars to complete one revolution. Sirius, the brightest visible star, is in fact a double star which has a period of 50 years and the two components are 20.5 AU apart. Thus

$$M + m = \frac{(20.5)^3}{(50)^2} = 3.44 \text{ solar masses.}$$

The combined mass of Sirius A (the bright component) and Sirius B (the small dark component) is equal to 3.44 times the mass of the sun.

It is also desirable to obtain the masses of the individual components of a binary star. This requires very careful measurement of the movement of these components around their common center of gravity. Applying the relationship used to find the mass of the moon (Section 3.4) makes it possible to determine the mass of the individual components once the total mass of a binary star is known.

Mass may also be determined for spectroscopic binaries, those binary stars that are so close that their components cannot be resolved with a telescope. These stars have high orbital velocities which can be detected by spectroscopic methods—hence their name. The masses of the components of spectroscopic binaries are obtained from indirect data but, as a statistic, serve a useful purpose.

When the mass of a star has been computed, it is possible to determine the density of the material of which the star is composed provided the size of the star is known. Density is the weight of a given volume of substance. The standard used is water which has a density of one gram per cubic centimeter. Since the mass and volume of the sun is known, the mean density can be calculated and is found to be 1.4 grams per cubic centimeter. This means that any given average volume of the sun weighs 1.4 times an equal volume of water. The density of the earth is 5.52 grams per cubic centimeter. While the variations in mass of the stars are generally limited to a narrow range, the density varies widely because of the wide range in stellar sizes. Many stars have densities much lower than that of water. In fact, densities for some stars have been determined to be lower than for the best vacuum obtainable on earth. Such a star is sometimes called a *hot vacuum*. Epsilon Aurigae, the largest star, has a density about one hundred-millionth that of water. Extremes of high densities have also been discovered. One of these is for Sirius B, which has a mass approximately equal to that of the sun (0.95) but is only about ⅟₃₀,₀₀₀ the size. This means that the same amount of matter which makes up the sun is compressed into a much smaller volume. The density of Sirius B, therefore, is almost one ton per cubic inch. This is not the densest star known. This record is held by a white dwarf star about 1700 miles in diameter, which has a density of almost 1600 tons per cubic inch.

4.6 STELLAR MOTION

The ancient Greeks believed that the stars were permanently fixed on a sphere which whirled around the earth in an east to west direction once each day. So slight is the motion of each star as measured with the unaided eye, that constellations today are essentially the same as when they were described 2000 years ago. In 1718, Halley compared star charts made by Hipparchus with catalogs of his day and found that Aldebaran, Arcturus, and Sirius had changed position. This meant that the distant stars were not firmly fixed but were movable as were the nearby planets. The apparent motion was extremely small because of the great distances involved. This motion was consistent with the requirements of Newton's Law of Gravity, since motion is necessary to keep objects from falling into each other.

Since Halley's discovery, the motions of many stars have been studied. The measurements require great precision and are complicated by the rotation of the earth, the revolution of the earth around the sun, the earth's precession, and the movement through space of the entire solar system.

The speed and direction of a star is found by measuring its radial velocity and proper motion. *Radial velocity* is the speed with which a star is moving toward or away from the earth and is obtained by means of a spectrograph. Light from the star in question is directed through a telescope into the opening of the spectrograph. The star's spectrum is photographed along with the comparison spectrum of iron. The velocity may be calculated as described in Section 2.5. Radial velocities of more than 10,000 stars have been measured in this manner; the velocity is expressed in miles or kilometers per second. It is designated positive if the star is moving away from the sun, and negative if it is moving toward the sun. It must be remembered that a complicating factor in making such a measurement is the fact that the sun is also moving. Thus, what is being measured is the speed with which the star and the sun are moving toward or away from each other. Stars, of course, vary in radial velocity but 20 miles per second is quite common. The highest velocity is over 400 miles per second.

The radial velocity is not the true velocity of a star nor does it indicate the true direction in which a star is moving. The *proper motion,* defined as the angular change in direction of a star in seconds of arc per year, must also be considered. Great precision is required because the annual movement is usually quite small. At the present time measurements of this type are made photographically by comparing star photos taken a number of years apart. Periods of from 20 to 50 years are not unusual. The displacement of a star over a period of years is a measure of the motion that has taken place.

The star with the highest known proper motion is Bernard's star, so named after its discoverer. It is the second closest star to the sun (after Alpha Centauri) at a distance of almost 6 light-years. It is invisible to the naked eye. The star's high velocity causes it to change its position by 10.25 seconds of arc per year. In Fig. 4.5, A represents a star as originally photographed from the earth. The proper motion is the displacement that has caused the star to appear to move from A to B. The actual direction taken by the star is represented by the movement from A to D. The velocity of motion from A to D can be calculated, but first it is necessary to determine the tangential velocity, or the velocity of the star in moving from A to B. For this purpose it is necessary not only to know its proper motion but also the distance of the star from the observer on earth. Then, with the aid of a simple formula derived for this calculation, the tangential velocity may be determined. This formula is expressed as follows:

$$\text{Velocity} = 2.95 \, \frac{\mu}{p} \text{ miles per second,}$$

where μ is the proper motion in seconds of arc and p is the distance in parsecs. From Fig. 4.5 it can be seen that the velocity of the star from A to B and A to C has been determined. It is now possible, by use of the Pythagorean Theorem, to calculate the space velocity over the star's actual path from A to D.

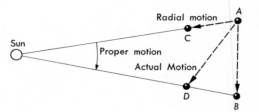

Fig. 4.5 Relationship of proper motion (AB), radial velocity (AC), and actual motion (AD) of a star with respect to the solar system.

The foregoing discussion has been on the basis of a star's motion relative to the sun as though the sun were motionless, which is not the case. That the sun moves* with respect to other stars was first realized by Herschel in the early nineteenth century. Astronomers at Greenwich had already measured the movement of 36 stars, but it was Herschel who caught the significance of the sun's motion and, by careful study, was able to show that it was in the direction of the constellation Hercules. Now, with better instruments, radial velocity and proper motion have been used to verify the sun's motion.

Proper motion has been defined as the angular displacement of a star with respect to the sun. This displacement is due in part to the star's movement and in part to the sun's movement. The proper motion of stars lying in the path of the sun, either at the

---

* The sun's motion in this context is that of the entire solar system.

apex of the sun's motion (direction toward which the sun is traveling), or the *antapex* of the sun's motion (point away from which the sun is moving), will be little influenced by solar motion. The stars at the apex would appear to be moving to the left and right as the sun approaches, much as the trees in a forest do as they are approached (Fig. 4.6). At the same time, the stars at the antapex would seem to be closing in behind as the sun moves away from them. The maximum effect of proper motion can be measured at points at right angles to the sun's direction of motion. Only those stars with velocities greater than that of the sun will show a proper motion in the same direction as the sun moves. Since these are few, the great majority will show a proper motion in a direction opposite to that of the sun; in other words, toward the antapex.

Radial velocity indicates not only the direction being taken by the sun but also the speed with which the sun is moving relative to the nearby stars. Radial velocity, it will be recalled, is the speed with which a star is approaching or receding from the sun. The velocity of stars traveling at right angles to the direction of the sun's motion is not influenced by the velocity of the sun. Since there are as many stars moving toward the sun moves. Since these are few, the great majority will show a proper motion in a the apex, the velocities average about −12 miles per second, which is an indication that the sun is moving toward them at approximately this speed. By the same token, the average velocity for stars at the antapex is +12 miles per second, confirming the sun's velocity and direction toward the apex. An analysis of the data on radial velocities and proper motion of nearby stars verifies the fact that the sun is approaching Vega (a star in the constellation Lyra slightly to the east of Hercules) at a velocity of 12 miles per second.

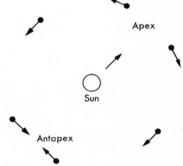

Fig. 4.6 The average proper motion of stars surrounding the sun provides a clue to the direction of motion of the sun through space.

4.7 STELLAR CLASSIFICATION

By the turn of the twentieth century, great progress had been made in astronomy, and attention was turned toward the classification of stars. The systematic organization of data on animal and plant life and on rocks and minerals based on similarities led inevitably to the question of similarities between stars. Were the stars all different or were there some common characteristics under which they could be assembled into logical groups? In 1863 Angelo Secchi classified the stars into four groups according to the arrangement of the dark lines on their spectra. Henry Draper later modified this system to include description of variations in star spectra not indicated by Secchi. E. C. Pickering of the Harvard Observatory developed a new method for obtaining improved images with the spectrograph which made it necessary to refine the classification in order to account for greater detail. This requirement led to the Harvard system of spectral classification which was based on the examination of more than 200,000 spectra by Miss A. J. Cannon, Miss A. C. Maury, and Mrs. W. P. Fleming. So many types were found that the system required the use of almost every letter in the alphabet. However, upon completion of the task it was found that 99% of the types fitted into about seven main spectral classes, and these constituted a temperature scale when properly rearranged. The colors of the stars ranged from blue, indicating high temperature, to red for low temperature. According to the letter designation originally ascribed to the different types, the spectral classes are denoted by the letters O, B, A, F, G, K, and M when placed in the order of highest to lowest temperature group. Spectral classification has proved to be a valuable device. Simply identifying the color of a star makes it possible to infer other characteristics such as temperature and prominent lines of certain elements in the spectrum of that star. Each of the spectral classes is divided into 10 subclasses and identi- fied by a number from 0 to 9 to indicate placement within each class. Thus, F5 indicates a position halfway between F and G. The sun is designated G2, meaning that it is 0.2 of the way from G0 to K0.

While the majority of the stars fit into the spectral classes just discussed, there are several additional groups prominent enough to be mentioned. For the most part these are similar to the stars in the main spectral classes. Certain characteristics place them in separate groupings which are branches of the main spectral classes. Thus, R-stars are a branch of class K, while N- and S-stars are a branch of class M. The spectral classes may be shown by symbols as follows:

$$\text{O—B—A—F—G—K—M} \begin{array}{c} \nearrow R \quad \nearrow N \\ \searrow S \end{array}$$

An examination of Table 4.2 could lead to the erroneous conclusion that stars are composed of different materials. Stars are made up primarily of hydrogen, with small amounts of helium and very small amounts of other elements. The diverse temperature conditions on stars result in different intensities of spectral lines, causing certain elements to be prominent at various places in the spectral scale. The fact that certain elements are prominent does not preclude the presence of the others.

4.8   THE HERTZSPRUNG-RUSSELL DIAGRAM

In 1905 the Danish astronomer, Einar Hertzsprung, considered the possibility of a correlation between the luminosity of a star and its spectral classification. By comparing a star's color and its luminosity he found that in general white and blue stars had high luminosity, and red stars low luminosity. He found some exceptions to this rule: a few red stars were also highly luminous, indicating great size. In 1913 an American astron- omer, Henry Russell, made a similar discovery and a combination of the two efforts resulted in the Hertzsprung-Russell or H-R diagram (Fig. 4.7) The abscissa of the diagram shows the spectral types which correspond to the temperature and color of a star, and the ordinate shows luminosity as related to the sun and the absolute magnitude.

Since each star was represented by a dot on the diagram, it soon became evident that the great majority of the stars of known distance fitted within a narrow band ranging from the hot, highly luminous stars to the relatively cool, dimmer stars. This band is called the main sequence. In the upper right-hand side of the diagram is a group of stars red in color but highly luminous, indicating great size. These have been designated as *giants* or *supergiants,* depending on the degree of luminosity. Around 1925 an additional group of stars, the *white dwarfs,* were discovered and placed in the lower left-hand quadrant of the diagram. It was felt that these stars must be small because, in spite of their white color, they yielded very little light. Approximately 89% of the stars within a radius of 150 light-years are on the main sequence, 9% are white dwarfs, 1% are giants or supergiants, and the remainder are variable stars which will be discussed later.

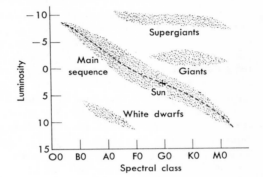

Fig. 4.7 The Hertzsprung-Russell diagram of about 1200 local stars.

The H-R diagram is more than an interesting array of facts based on luminosity, distance, and temperature. It is a device which enables astronomers to make valid comparisons of the stars and learn something about the life history of a star. For example, all yellow stars on the main sequence have been found to be similar with respect to mass, stars that are white to blue have greater mass than yellow stars, and red stars have less mass. This evidence led to a new relationship between mass and luminosity, namely that stars with greater mass are more highly luminous. The degree of luminosity is not directly related to mass, however, for if the mass is twice as great, the luminosity may be increased tenfold. A star that is 5 times the mass of the sun may be 50 or more times as bright as the sun and use up its available fuel 50 times as fast. From this it is possible to conclude that bright massive stars are short-lived compared to the sun. Information such as this makes it possible to estimate stellar age.

In recent decades the observation of certain star clusters has aided in studying the life histories of stars. Star clusters are homogeneous groupings of stars which are acting as a unit in that they are moving in the same direction and at the same velocity. Two main types of clusters are recognized. The open or galactic cluster is usually composed of a few to a thousand or so stars rather widely spaced, so that individual members are easily definable. Typical among the galactic clusters are such well-known groups as the Pleiades and the Hyades. There are about 500 such clusters known in the Milky Way galaxy. The other type is the globular cluster, much more compact, made up of about 100,000 stars, and much more distant from the earth than the galactic clusters. It is not possible to see them with the unaided eye. About 100 globular clusters have been located, some within the galaxy, some beyond it. An example is the cluster Messier 13 in Hercules, which is about 25,000 light-years away and which contains upward of 100,000 stars in a compact mass. Although appearing to be an almost solid mass, the average distance between the stars is about one light-year and, even in the dense center, the stars are thousands of astronomical units apart. The probability of collision is thought to be practically zero although their close proximity could disturb the orbit of outer planets if any exist.

Studying the stars in a cluster has several advantages. First, it may be assumed that the stars in a cluster were formed at approximately the same time and are, therefore, all of about the same age. The second advantage is the fact that stars in a cluster are all about the same distance from an observer on earth. Therefore, a star which appears 100 times brighter than another in the same cluster must have a greater mass since distance is not a factor. An H-R diagram of a cluster may be somewhat different than the H-R diagram for local stars in Fig. 4.7. An open cluster in the constellation Serpens (Messier 16), for example, shows a preponderance of massive blue stars but no white, yellow, or red stars. Since stars of high mass are short-lived, existing for as little as 25 to 30 million years, it may be concluded that the stars are as yet very young. On the other hand, an open cluster in the constellation of Cancer (Messier 44), lacks the massive blue stars in the H-R diagram and contains only white, yellow, and red stars. The only stars left are those which last a long time, which indicates that these are middle-aged stars. The globular cluster in Hercules (Messier 13), previously mentioned, is older yet, showing no blue or white stars. Only the yellow stars (like the sun) and the red stars are still present. Those stars which remain are very old, and all the large bright stars have disappeared.

4.9 UNUSUAL STARS

The sun may be considered a normal star, one about which a great deal is known and one which has no unusual characteristics. Most of the stars in the main sequence may be considered normal, differing only in luminosity, mass, and temperature but conforming fairly well to a recognizable pattern. There are a few other types of stars which do not fit into the typical pattern, and these atypical stars should be commented on before we turn to a discussion of stellar evolution.

Several unusual types appear on the H-R diagram, among them the red giants and supergiants located in the upper right-hand quadrant of the diagram. These are, with few exceptions, Type K or M stars, lying above the main sequence and of high luminosity. Betelgeuse and Antares are examples of supergiants, while Arcturus and Capella are typical of giants.

White dwarfs are extremely small stars, having a color similar to spectral Type A stars but only about $\frac{1}{100,000}$ as bright. These stars are placed below and to the left of the main sequence on the H-R diagram. Their luminosity is faint due to their small size, and they are invisible to the naked eye. White dwarfs are noted for their high density (Section 4.5) which is due to their small size and large mass. Only a few hundred have been discovered, and most of these were found because of their association with larger stars in a binary system.

Certain variable or pulsating stars (Section 4.1) exist which are thought to be characteristic of one stage in the evolution of a star. The first such star was discovered in 1784 by an English astronomer, John Goodricke. He found that Delta Cephei varied in magnitude between 4.1 and 5.2 in a period of 5.4 days. Recent studies have shown that there are actually three main types of variable stars. Cepheid I stars have an absolute magnitude of approximately 3 to 6 and periods ranging from 1.5 to 40 days. These stars brighten rapidly and dim gradually. The Cepheid II stars are about 1.5 magnitudes dimmer than Cepheid I types, and have periods ranging from 10 to 30 days. The brightening and dimming of these stars occur at a more gradual rate and the light curve is more irregular than that of the Type I Cepheids. R R-Lyrae variables are short-period variables having periods of less than a day, typically from 7 to 17 hours.

A more spectacular form of variable is the nova. A *nova* is an existing star which erupts suddenly and violently, increasing in brightness many thousands of times. The brightness declines to prenova stage at a much slower rate, in some cases taking years to return to normal. The exact cause of the outburst is unknown, but it appears that an outer layer of gas is ejected at velocities reaching 1000 miles per second. This expanding shell of gas is responsible for the increase in brightness. A few novae have been observed to have more than one outburst without apparent damage. There is no way of predicting when one will occur. On the average, two to three novae have been discovered telescopically each year, but many may escape detection since a constant vigil is not kept on all parts of the sky at all times. Most of the novae have occurred in the spectral type O or B stars rather than in the relatively cool Type-G stars, such as the sun. This does not completely eliminate the prospect that a Type-G star may become a nova, but the chances are much reduced.

Another type of eruptive variable is the *supernova*, much rarer than the nova but much more cataclysmic. Where the nova flares up to thousands of times its normal brightness, the supernova will become tens or even hundreds of thousands of times brighter than normal. The gas shell expands away from the star at velocities of up to 3000 miles per second, and the material ejected in this shell may constitute a major portion of the star. Three supernovae have been observed during the past 1000 years: one was recorded by the Chinese in 1054, one was observed by Tycho Brahe in 1572, and one was seen by Kepler and Galileo in 1604. Now supernovae are observed in other galaxies and are thought to occur in a galaxy about once every few hundred years.

4.10 STELLAR EVOLUTION

All the bits and pieces of stellar information that culminated in the H-R diagram have contributed to the development of theories on the life history of stars. The first interpretation of the diagram given by Russell himself was essentially as follows: The star initially formed from a dark cloud of dust and gas into a red giant. The new star contracted and became steadily brighter as it moved up the main sequence to yellow, white, and blue positions on the diagram. The star gradually used up its nuclear fuel, reversed its position on the diagram as the temperature finally cooled, and ended up as a red dwarf at the lower right-hand end of the main sequence. This explanation implied that the sun was a relatively young star ascending toward the bright end of the sequence or a relatively old star descending toward the lower end of the sequence. Neither is the case; subsequent data gave evidence that stars may begin their life cycle anywhere on the main sequence.

A star forms in much the same manner as did the solar system (Section 3.2). A nebula, a cloud of dust and gas, begins to condense and collect as a result of mutual gravitational attraction. As the gas concentrates, more material is attracted to it, and the entire mass begins to take on a spherical shape. With continued contraction resulting from the embryonic star's own gravitational force, temperatures and densities rise. Part of the energy produced is converted to heat in the star's interior, and part is radiated as light, heat, and radio waves. At this point the infant star is born (Fig. 4.8).

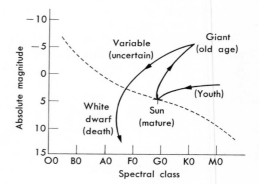

Fig. 4.8 Pathway of possible stellar evolution on Hertzsprung-Russell diagram.

The place occupied by the star on the main sequence is dependent on its mass. Stars of high mass (relative to the sun) will take a position in the upper left-hand portion of the H-R diagram and become hot short-lived stars, while stars with small mass will be relatively cool long-lived stars at the lower end of the main sequence. A star spends the major portion of its life on the main sequence; its hydrogen is being converted to helium with a release of energy (Section 3.4). The star at this point remains reasonably stable, for the heat energy produced in the interior is causing an expansion which is counteracted by the gravitational force exerted by the mass of the star. When the hydrogen fuel is diminished by perhaps 15%, this stability is upset. Whereas the nuclear reactions were taking place mainly at the core during the stable period, the reactions now shift to a shell around the core, causing the star to expand greatly to become a giant or supergiant, depending on its initial mass. This shifts the placement of the star to the right of the main sequence on the H-R diagram. Interior temperatures increase to perhaps 100 million degrees. The helium core, formed as a result of the conversion of hydrogen but inert up to this point, ignites at this high temperature to form a new source of fuel. In this new reaction three helium nuclei are thought to combine to form carbon. This activity results in additional changes in the star and is looked upon as the end of the red giant stage in the life cycle.

There is considerable uncertainty as to what occurs next, but it is thought that the star's position on the H-R diagram is reversed and that it returns to a main sequence position somewhat higher than its previous position and, at this point, becomes a variable star. During this period other heavier elements are being formed as a result of the extremely high temperatures in the star's interior. The star continues to shrink, its position dropping below the main sequence, and it becomes a white dwarf. The star may possibly go through a nova or supernova stage before becoming a white dwarf. This is thought to be true for stars having a mass greater than 1.4 times that of the sun. The excess mass is shed in a series of nova eruptions, or the star is almost completely destroyed as a supernova. White dwarfs are formed of "degenerate matter" made up of atoms in which the electrons have collapsed into the atomic nucleus, causing very close packing of the atoms. The nuclear fuel is exhausted, and the feeble light of the white dwarf is dependent on the residual heat from the interior which may last for as long as a billion years. The light from a white dwarf becomes progressively dimmer until nothing remains but a dense, dark, burned-out stellar clinker.

The debris resulting from a nova or supernova again becomes part of the dust and gas found in interstellar space. Having once been part of a star, the debris consists of the heavier elements as well as the residual hydrogen and helium. This material combines with interstellar hydrogen so that subsequent stars formed from this enriched dust and gas will have a greater proportion of heavy elements than stars formed in the past. Old stars in the galaxy have a lower proportion of heavy elements than younger stars, a fact leading some astronomers to the conclusion that the original stars in the galaxy were composed of pure hydrogen. The build-up of heavy elements from these original stars and the formation of new stars from this material has resulted in second- and possibly even third- generation stars in the galaxy. Heavy elements are detected in the sun, and since these elements could not yet have been formed, the sun is considered to be at least a second-generation star which has been formed from the debris of previously existing stars.

The sun will undoubtedly follow the same path as other stars and become a white dwarf. What will become of the solar system when this occurs? In the process of leaving the main sequence and becoming a red giant, the sun will expand at least to the orbit of Mercury and increase 100 times in brightness. Temperatures on earth will possibly reach 700°F to 800°F, causing the oceans to boil away and all life on earth to disappear. Eventually as the sun reaches the white-dwarf stage it will be about the present size of the earth. At this stage the sun will be about 100 times brighter than the light we see reflected by the full moon. The earth itself will be extremely cold, with the recondensed oceans frozen solid. Many of the now familiar stars will have disappeared and have been replaced by young stars. Of the planets, only those that are nearby will reflect the dim sunlight.

4.11 THE CONSTELLATIONS

Many stars are easily visible to an observer on the earth. They appear to be scattered haphazardly across the sky. Upon closer examination, certain patterns become evident, and these patterns led the ancient astronomers to conceive of the constellations. The *constellations,* representing figures that are figments of man's imagination, have been handy points of reference for locating particular celestial bodies. Today's professional astronomer, aiming his telescope to locate a particular object or star which he may not even be able to see, must have more precise data. But for the amateur, the constellations still serve this purpose very nicely.

The geometric patterns in which the stars are arranged were named after gods and goddesses and mythological animals, but have little or no resemblance to these figures.

Some people think that no more resemblance was intended than exists in modern times when a geographic location is named after some person. No record exists as to who named the constellations, but it is believed that the 48 constellations listed in Ptolemy's catalog had been recognized for some 3000 years. These are visible only in the Northern Hemisphere and do not include stars seen in the southern sky.

Tycho Brahe added two new constellations in the seventeenth century. Since then new ones have been discovered, bringing the present total to 88. Of these, 70 are visible in the Northern Hemisphere.

The constellations themselves have no astronomical significance except as a means of identifying the location of an individual star, galaxy, nebula, or nova. Traditionally, a celestial object is said to be "in" some constellation. This does not mean that the object is a part of the constellation. It merely indicates that the object has this constellation as a background or can be seen through the constellation.

Stars and other celestial objects are frequently named for the constellation in which they are found. Usually the brightest star in the constellation is designated by the Greek letter alpha followed by the genitive form of the name of the constellation. Other stars were then assigned Greek letters in decreasing order of brightness, although there are exceptions to this rule. In 1729 a system was adopted in which the stars in a constellation were numbered consecutively from west to east across the constellation regardless of brightness. As more powerful instruments were developed this, too, became inadequate. Stars are now cataloged by number and position.

The best way to learn the stars is to have someone point them out in relation to the constellation in which they are found. Others may then be found with the aid of star charts (see pages 86–92).

4.12   SUMMARY

Despite the great distances between the stars and the earth, diligent effort on the part of astronomers has resulted in the accumulation of many data relating to distance, temperature, luminosity, size, mass, and color. The data have made possible the classification of stars into types based on remarkable similarities. This system of classification has been most useful in the development of the Hertzsprung-Russell diagram which relates type of star to absolute magnitude. The diagram has enabled astronomers to draw some conclusions with respect to the relationship between the mass of a star and its brightness. It has shown, for example, that the brighter stars also have greater mass. The age of stars has been inferred since it had been theoretically calculated that brighter stars used up their nuclear fuel at a much faster rate relative to their mass than did dimmer stars. Certain stages of a star's life cycle have also been deduced from the H-R diagram. It is believed that a star originally forms from a contracting cloud of gas and takes a position on the main sequence depending on its size and temperature. The major portion of a star's life is spent in this phase. Hydrogen is converted to helium, and eventually the star becomes unstable and begins to expand to form a red giant. What takes place in the stage following this is not well understood, but it is surmised that the star shrinks, possibly becoming a variable star, and that formation of some of the heavier elements takes place. Following this, the star may explode, lose mass, and eventually become a white dwarf.

While not an exact means of locating stars, the constellations have served many hundreds of years as a guide to the stars for amateurs and professionals alike. Great satisfaction can be gained by recognition of stars and constellations. Identification can be achieved with just a minimum of practice.

SUGGESTED READINGS

ABELL, G., *Exploration of the Universe.* New York: Holt, Rinehart and Winston, 1964.

BOK, B. J. and P., *The Milky Way.* Cambridge, Mass.: Harvard University Press, 1957.

CAMPBELL, L., and L. JACCHIA, *The Story of the Variable Stars.* New York: McGraw-Hill, 1941.

GAMOW, G., *The Birth and Death of the Sun.* New York: New American Library, 1952.

GOLDBERG, L., and L. H. ALLER, *Atoms, Stars and Nebula.* New York: McGraw-Hill, 1946.

KRUSE W., and W. DIECKVOSS, *The Stars.* Ann Arbor, Mich.: University of Michigan Press, 1957.

STAR CHARTS*

These maps show the principal stars and planets which are above the horizon at latitude 34° north at about 9 P.M. standard time at the middle of the months for which they are drawn. Each may be used anywhere in the United States throughout the entire month, and shows the sky at 10 P.M. on the first and at 8 P.M. on the last of the month. To use one, hold it vertically and turn it so that the point of the compass toward which you are facing shows on the bottom of the map.

* From C. H. Cleminshaw, "Monthly Star Maps," Griffith Observatory and Planetarium, Los Angeles. Reprinted by permission.

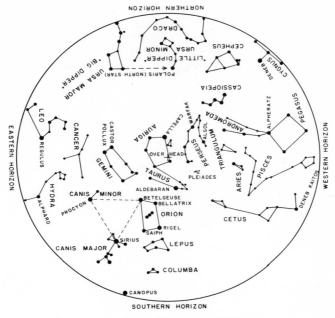

THE NIGHT SKY IN JANUARY

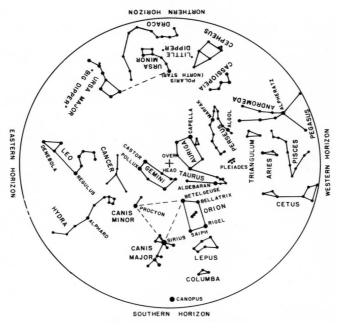

THE NIGHT SKY IN FEBRUARY

THE NIGHT SKY IN MARCH

THE NIGHT SKY IN APRIL

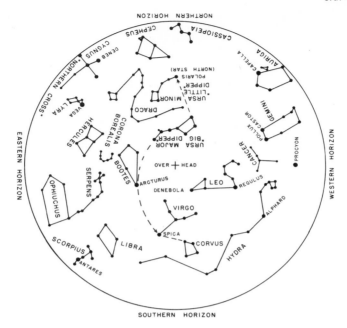

THE NIGHT SKY IN MAY

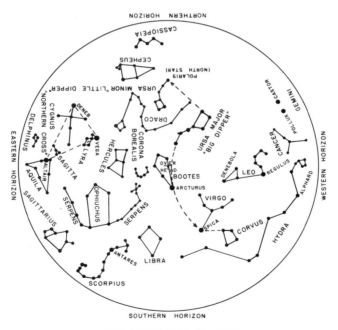

THE NIGHT SKY IN JUNE

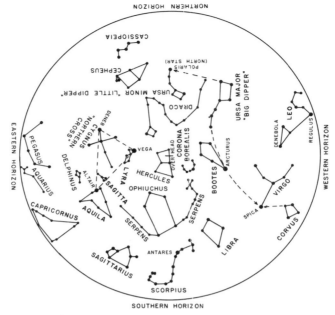

THE NIGHT SKY IN JULY

THE NIGHT SKY IN AUGUST

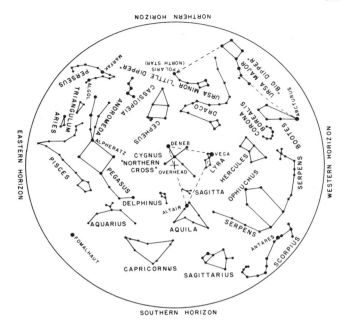

THE NIGHT SKY IN SEPTEMBER

THE NIGHT SKY IN OCTOBER

THE NIGHT SKY IN NOVEMBER

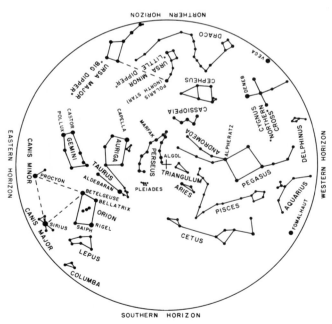

THE NIGHT SKY IN DECEMBER

CHAPTER 5

GALAXIES

The sun, all the visible stars, and the billions of stars visible through a telescope make up an aggregate of stars which, together with nebulae, form a flat spiral structure called a galaxy (Fig. 5.1). *Gala* is a Greek word for milk and was first applied by the Greeks to the broad band of faint light caused by billions of distant stars extending through the constellations Sagittarius, Cygnus, Cassiopeia, Auriga, and Canis Major. The faint light of the galaxy is visible only on clear moonless nights far from the artificial illumination found near a city.

5.1 THE GALAXY DISCOVERED

Galileo was the first to identify the Milky Way as a band of numerous stars at tremendous distances from the earth. However, it was Thomas Wright, a former sailor, who around the middle of the eighteenth century first questioned the arrangement of the stars. He saw what others before him had seen, a myriad of stars overhead with a faint band of light passing through the dark sky representing what appeared to be a much denser population of stars. Wright raised the question of whether the density was really greater in the Milky Way, or whether the stars were just as far apart there as in other parts of the sky. He felt that observers were looking broadside through a lens-shaped structure which acted to give the illusion of greater density. This was a revolutionary idea. It seemed strange that in the hundreds of years of viewing by thousands of observers, the same idea had not previously occurred to someone. Wright was able to show the structure of the star system in its true form, a lens-shaped system rather than a sphere, and his reasoning was difficult to refute.

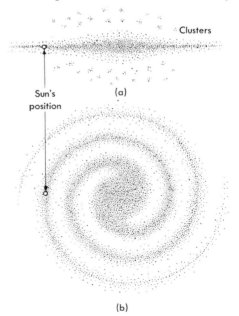

Fig. 5.1 (a) Cross section and (b) plane view of the Milky Way.

93

Immanuel Kant, along with his other accomplishments, found time in 1753 to examine Wright's discovery. He made several unusual observations which bordered on the prophetic. He compared the form of the galaxy, as described by Wright, with that of the solar system. Both were flat, circular-shaped structures. Since the stars had been shown to move, Kant speculated about the possibility that the stars in the galaxy revolved around a center, and that therefore the entire galactic structure turned like some gigantic wheel. Kant also felt that there was no reason why the universe should be limited to only one such galaxy. A number of faint oval-shaped nebulosities had already been observed through telescopes, and Kant thought these might represent distant galaxies similar to the Milky Way. With this reasoning, Kant greatly extended man's concept of the universe and perhaps prompted Johann Heinrich Lambert, in 1761, to stretch this concept to infinity. The question of whether the universe is finite or infinite has still not been resolved.

William Herschel hoped to prove Wright's theory on the structure of the galaxy. His approach was to count stars systematically to determine the density of number in selected positions of the sky. He sampled 3400 spots, using a 12-inch reflecting telescope, and concluded that the galaxy was irregularly disk-shaped rather than lens-shaped and that the sun was off to one side from the galactic center.

5.2 SHAPE, SIZE, AND POPULATION OF THE MILKY WAY

The modern view of the Milky Way is about as shown in Fig. 5.1. Much of this was determined by Harlow Shapley who, in 1917, mapped the position of a number of globular clusters associated with the Milky Way. From their distribution, he was able to infer to some extent the shape and also the size of the galaxy. This flat disk-shaped structure with the bulge at the center is about 100,000 light-years in diameter and 10,000 light-years thick through the bulge. The sun is close to the equatorial plane of the galaxy and much farther off to one side than was envisioned by Herschel; it is about 30,000 light-years from the center, or about two-thirds of the distance from the galactic center.

The total number of stars may be estimated by star counts in representative portions of the galaxy. Herschel first attempted to do this. He assumed that the brightest stars were also the closest and that the stars were uniformly distributed in space. The actual count did not agree with calculated numbers once he got beyond the place he believed was occupied by stars of magnitude 3. He had approached the problem correctly but had no way of measuring the true brightness of the stars. At the beginning of the twentieth century, this technique was again applied, and although the true brightness of the stars could then be measured, galactic dust obscured many stars and made the count at great distances unreliable. Present-day counts, allowing corrections for the effects of galactic dust, estimate the number of stars in the Milky Way galaxy at about 100 billion.

5.3 GALACTIC MOTION

In previous chapters we described the motion of the planets about the sun and the motion of the sun with respect to neighboring stars. Those stars with observable space velocities are relatively close to the sun, usually within a few thousand light-years. The motion of these stars does not reflect their motion as part of the galaxy, but only their motion relative to the sun. In other words, this motion of about 12 to 20 miles per second reflects only slight differences in direction and placement of these stars within the galaxy. At the same time the neighboring stars along with the sun move in a circular path or orbit around the center of the galaxy at a speed of approximately 150 miles per second. This true motion of the sun can be determined only by making observation on very distant objects which do not share in this motion. These objects are distant external globular clusters which do, in fact, move but are not rotating with the galaxy. The motion in this instance is determined in much the same manner as the motion and direction of the sun are determined with respect to local stars. Here, again, in one direction the globular cluster appears to be approaching the sun, and in the other direction to be receding from the sun. Still more evidence of galactic rotation may be obtained by studying the motion of external neighboring galaxies with respect to the sun. Studies of this type reveal that the Large Magellanic Cloud is receding from the sun at a velocity of about 170 miles per second, while the great Andromeda galaxy is approaching the sun with a velocity of about 190 miles per second. These velocities are not so much evidence of galactic motion as they are an indication of the motion of the sun within the Milky Way. In fact, these velocities would indicate that local galaxies are moving more or less at random and that their velocities with respect to each other are quite low.

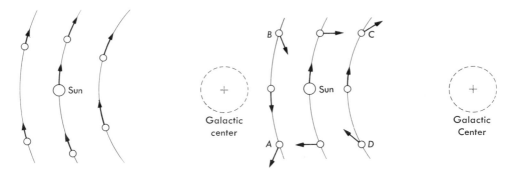

Fig. 5.2 Movement of stars around the galactic center.

Fig. 5.3 Relative movement of stars as seen from stationary sun.

Does the galaxy rotate as a giant wheel with all stars maintaining the same relative position? This would imply much higher velocities for stars farther from the galactic center. Or do the stars revolve around the center in the manner of the planets around the sun, with the inner stars moving at higher velocities than those farther out? The latter seems to be the answer, based on studies of star motions. The motion of the stars around the center of the galaxy is shown in Fig. 5.2. The sun along with the stars in its orbit moves at a slower velocity than do the stars closer to the galactic center, and it moves along at a higher velocity than those stars farther from the center. How would this motion appear if the sun were stationary? This is illustrated in Fig. 5.3 where the sun is shown in relation to the stars in surrounding constellations. In this instance the sun's velocity has been subtracted from the velocity of the surrounding stars. The stars ahead of the sun in its orbit have practically no radial velocity and have a proper motion very slightly toward the galactic center. Those stars in orbit behind the sun also exhibit no radial velocity and only slight proper motion away from the galactic center, indicating movement along an arc. Stars in position *A* appear to be moving away from the sun, since they are behind the sun and are moving more slowly. Stars in position *C* also appear to be moving away from the sun because they are moving at higher velocity and are preceding the sun in their path around the galactic center. Stars in position *B* and *D* appear to be moving toward the sun, but Figs. 5.2 and 5.3 show that this motion is again the result of direction and speed with respect to the sun.

Determining the speed and direction of objects in space is a complex task. Reference points from which measurements are made are themselves in motion and this motion in turn is difficult to define. The accuracy of any space measurement is open to argument, but the margin of error is probably not more than 20% to 25%. Thus, the velocity of the sun in orbit in the galaxy may be higher or lower than the 150 miles per second. This is a reasonable figure, however, and coupled with the distance from the galactic center, also not precisely known, yields an approximate period of revolution for the sun of about 220 million years.

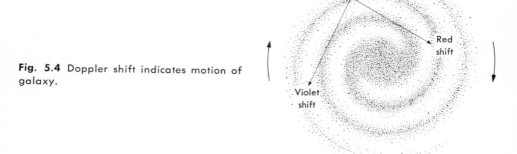

Fig. 5.4 Doppler shift indicates motion of galaxy.

Additional data on galactic rotation have been obtained by the use of the radio telescope. Stars on the opposite side of the galaxy which are obscured by nebulae and are too dim for optical telescopic examination, can be examined by radio means. Evidence of galactic rotation is obtained by measuring the Doppler shift of radiation which indicates movement away from the sun on one side of the galaxy and toward the sun from the other side (Fig. 5.4). Radio examination of the galaxy has also contributed greatly to studies on the structure of galaxies.

5.4   GALACTIC STRUCTURE

The shape of the Milky Way has been described as a flat disk with a bulging nucleus, but this picture of the structure is not strictly accurate. By studying the many forms of external galaxies, astronomers could see various possibilities and soon suspected that the Milky Way was in fact a spiral galaxy. An examination of external spiral galaxies has revealed that most of the brightest stars (usually also the youngest) and the interstellar material are located in the spiral arms. These conditions appear to exist in the Milky Way with mainly Type-O and Type-B stars and nebulae in the outer reaches of the galaxy. Because of the sun's position in one of these arms surrounded by interstellar dust, it is difficult to see any great part of even the neighboring arms. Only in the last decade has a study of distant nebulae enabled astronomers to partially map the spiral arms and find that the sun is located on the inner edge of an arm known as the *Orion arm,* named for the Orion nebula (Fig. 5.5). The arms are about 6000 to 7000 light-years apart and extend about 2500 light-years from the inner to the outer edge. The central bulge of the galaxy is about 4500 light-years in diameter. The innermost arm of the disk portion of the galaxy is about 15,000 light-years from the galactic center. The second arm is about 21,000 light-years from the center, and the third arm (the Orion arm) is about 27,000 light-years from the center. A fourth arm, the *Perseus arm,* at 35,000 light-years and a faint fifth arm about 45,000 light-years from the galactic center complete the structure. More recent radio data obtained in the Netherlands and Australia indicate that the arms show breaks and branching in the actual structure.

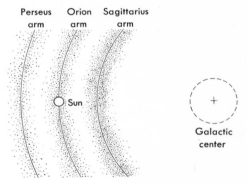

Fig. 5.5 Spiral arm structure in the vicinity of the sun.

Surrounding the nucleus and the disk of the galaxy is a spherical *halo* made up of globular clusters, a few isolated pulsating stars, and a tenuous cloud of hydrogen gas. The objects in the halo do not participate in the galactic motion but have movements of their own. The orbits of these objects around the galactic center are thought to be elliptical in some cases, with one of the focal points of the ellipse coinciding with the center of the galaxy. The radius of the halo appears to be about 60,000 light-years from the galactic center.

An interesting feature about the nature of the stars in the galaxy was discovered during World War II by W. Baade of the Mount Wilson Observatory. He found that, in general, stars in the outer arms of the galaxy were bright hot stars, Types O and B, which he designated Population I stars, and those toward the center were dimmer and redder, which he named Population II stars. By comparison, Population I stars contained more of the heavier elements than Population II stars and were relatively young stars, while Population II stars contained less of the heavy elements and were quite old. Examination of the Andromeda galaxy, a neighboring galaxy similar to the Milky Way, showed that the same circumstances existed there, with older (Population II) stars toward the center and newer (Population I) stars in the arms. Since that time the nature of stars has been found to be so complex that it is impossible to fit them neatly into two categories. At a conference in Rome in 1957, astronomers agreed on a system of classification dividing stars into five populations as follows:

1. Extreme Population I includes stars that are less than a few tens of millions of years old and dust and gas not yet formed into stars. Rigel in the constellation of Orion is an example of such a star which lies in the spiral arms.

2. Intermediate Population I stars are from a hundred million to a few billion years old. These stars are not necessarily restricted to the spiral arms but for the most part are found there.

3. Disk Population stars are from three to five billion years old and are located mainly between the central mass of the galaxy and the outer spiral arms. Most of the stars in the galaxy are of this type, including the sun. The chemical composition of these stars indicates that most are second- or third- generation stars made up of the debris of pre-existing stars.

4. Intermediate Population II stars are a little older than the previous group and occupy the fringes of the central mass of the galaxy. Stars which act as novae appear to belong to this group.

5. Extreme Population II stars are the oldest in the galaxy, being at least seven to eight billion years old. They make up the stars of the central mass, the globular clusters, and stars in the halo.

Obviously there is some overlapping from one category to the next, since no clear-cut division can be designated. The system does provide, however, a convenient grouping for interpreting the characteristics of star populations in galaxies. For simplicity, the Population I and II designations are still frequently used to differentiate between objects in the spiral arms and objects other than those in the spiral arms.

5.5   GALACTIC MASS

How much matter is present in the galaxy? Some concept of the number of stars can be obtained by determining the amount of matter in the galaxy. In calculating the mass of a double star system, Newton's modification of Kepler's Third Law proved to be invaluable. The same technique may be used here by measuring the gravitational effect of the galaxy as a whole upon the sun. This gravitational force manifests itself in the relationship between the distance from the galactic center and the speed with which the sun revolves around the center. An assumption must be made that gravitational force acts as though the galactic mass were concentrated at the center. However, the value for mass obtained by using Kepler's Third Law compares favorably with that for the mass adjusted by many factors to account for the fact that the total mass is not at the center. This value is approximately 1.4×10^{11} or 140 billion times the mass of the sun. The problem involved in making such a computation is that the distance from the galactic center is only an approximation, as is the period of rotation of the sun around this center. These factors, along with the assumption that the mass is concentrated at the center, make the value for the galactic mass only a rough estimate. However, all available information places the value between 10^{11} and 2×10^{11} times the mass of the sun which is satisfactory for our purposes.

5.6 GALACTIC EVOLUTION

Studying what is known of the life cycle of stars and the motion and structure of galaxies offers some clues as to the possible evolution of galaxies. The age of the sun is about 5 to 6 billion years and may be considered the minimum possible age of the galaxy. If the sun had been formed during the early stages of galactic development, it would be made up primarily of hydrogen forming into helium. Since, however, it is known that the sun contains heavy elements it must be a second- or third-generation star formed from material ejected from earlier stars by the nova or supernova mechanism. Thus it is permissible to surmise that the galaxy is much older, possibly 10 billion years old.

Stars began their life cycle as a cloud of interstellar material which started to rotate and condense, eventually generating sufficient energy to initiate a thermonuclear reaction. In the initial stages, it is presumed that the protogalaxy was a huge tenuous mass of hydrogen and that no stars had as yet formed. As the great mass of turbulent gas rotated, internal gravitational forces caused the mass to begin to contract. As contraction took place and rotational speed increased, the density of the gases increased. Turbulence within the mass and the force of gravity made some gas eddies sufficiently dense to hold together and evolve into first-generation stars. These first stars may have formed in isolated groups, becoming the globular clusters which orbit around the galactic center. Others may have formed as individual stars with eccentric orbits about the galactic center.

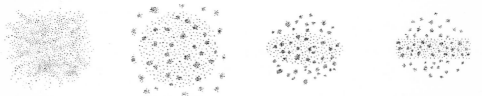

Fig. 5.6 Localized version of galactic structure. (Solidly dotted areas indicate regions of contracting gas.)

At this early stage of development, the galaxy had not yet taken on a disk-like structure, but as the gas condensed further and speed of rotation increased, the system began to flatten (Fig. 5.6). Only a small amount of the primordial hydrogen was utilized to form the first-generation stars, but the more massive ones quickly converted their fuel to helium and the heavier elements were formed. The hydrogen continued to contract and its density continued to increase, thereby improving conditions for star development. The number of stars which took shape increased, and these constituted second-generation stars, since the dust and gas from which they were formed included some of the heavier elements formed in the earlier stars. The disk now formed no longer contracted toward the galactic nucleus but further flattened, and the older

Population I stars, including the sun, were born. This was probably the period during which the greatest amount of star development was taking place. These stars contained greater quantities of heavier elements than those previously formed.

The sun is now believed to be 5 to 6 billion years old and many stars have been born since then, although at a reduced pace. The density of gas available now is much lower, estimated at about 1% to 2% of the total galactic mass. Most of this gas is confined to the outer arms of the galaxy and mainly on the equatorial plane of the disk. The stars being formed at present are, at the very least, third-generation stars with very high concentrations of heavy elements.

What will be the eventual fate of the galaxy? If the evolutionary path of a star and the development of the galaxy are as theorized, then the ultimate end of the galaxy can be predicted. A star goes through a life cycle which terminates in the formation of a white dwarf (Section 4.11). Only a small percentage of the material that originally went into the star is returned to interstellar space for the development of future stars. Thus, eventually all galactic material will be tied up in white dwarfs which, as they lose their energy, become black dwarfs or completely lifeless bodies. Ultimately there will be insufficient gas and dust in the interstellar spaces to form new stars, and those that remain will gradually die out to become dense, dark bodies which continue to orbit the galactic center.

In the last days of the galactic life cycle, the night sky will be almost completely dark except for a scattering of dim red stars and a few very dim specks of light indicating the location of the neighboring galaxies. The star around which a planet orbits will be a dim and extremely dense white dwarf radiating its last remaining bit of energy before extinction. The galaxy then will become a vast invisible structure moving undetected through endless space, but maintaining its internal structure and its position with respect to other galaxies.

5.7 TYPES OF GALAXIES

Beyond the Milky Way lie countless other galaxies so distant that the light from even the nearer ones started on its journey toward earth long before the dawn of man's recorded history. With characteristic thoroughness scientists have classified these many galaxies into a few categories for convenience. Basically there are three types which will be described briefly (Fig. 5.7).

1. Spiral galaxies (Fig. 5.7a) are by far the most common type of the distinctly visible galaxies, making up slightly more than 70% of the total number studied. The Milky Way is a typical one wherein the arms attached to a central nucleus radiate outward, giving a pinwheel effect. A barred spiral differs in that it is not nearly so compact as the normal spiral, and the arms emanate from a "bar" which passes through the center of the galaxy (Fig. 5.7b). The spiral galaxies are usually quite large, ranging from 20,000 to more than 125,000 light-years in diameter. The Milky Way and Andromeda are examples of the larger spiral galaxies.

2. Elliptical galaxies are generally smaller than spirals, and while much less common among the 1000 or so conspicuous galaxies, they are thought to be the most numerous type of galaxy in the universe. Their comparatively small diameter (as little as 5000 light-years) and therefore relatively low luminosity make them difficult to detect at

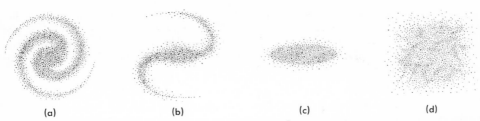

Fig. 5.7 Types of galaxies: (a) normal spiral, (b) barred spiral, (c) elliptical, (d) irregular.

great distances. While most elliptical galaxies are small, there are some exceptions. Several elliptical galaxies have been discovered which are much larger than any of the spirals. These may be as much or more than 200,000 light-years in diameter, being among the largest such structures in space.

The shape of elliptical galaxies ranges from an almost spherical form to the flat ellipse shown in Fig. 5.7(c). The population of stars is concentrated in the center and becomes sparse as the rim of the galaxy is reached. Elliptical galaxies are made up entirely of Population II stars and, therefore, resemble the nucleus of the spiral galaxies.

3. Irregular galaxies (Fig. 5.7d) make up about 5% of the total galactic population and are, as the name implies, lacking in symmetry. The Magellanic Clouds, visible from the earth's southern hemisphere near the south celestial pole, are typical of irregular galaxies. These are the external galaxies closest to the Milky Way, being approximately 150,000 light-years distant. Spectrographic analysis of these galaxies reveals interstellar gas and dust and Type-O and Type-B stars spread throughout the entire structure. This would indicate a relatively young age for these galaxies, a fact inconsistent with other evidence. Some globular clusters and certain individual stars that are old Population I (Disk Population) or even Population II stars, are present in the Magellanic Clouds.

The difference in structure and to some extent an apparent difference in age have prompted some astronomers to conclude that galaxies go through a sequence of stages during their evolutionary development. Edwin Hubble, during the 1920's, suggested such a sequence as the one illustrated in Fig. 5.8. He envisioned the elliptical galaxies starting as spheres and gradually flattening into elliptical disks. Subsequently arms would form, transforming the elliptical galaxies into normal and barred spirals, each developing along a different path.

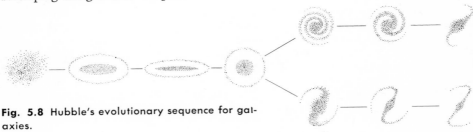

Fig. 5.8 Hubble's evolutionary sequence for galaxies.

A more modern version, presented by Harlow Shapley, suggests that the galactic life cycle begins with an irregular galaxy made up of young stars and then branches into the normal and barred spirals (Fig. 5.9). Continued contraction of the spiral structure eventually eliminates the arms, whereupon the galaxy becomes elliptical with no arms and only Population II stars.

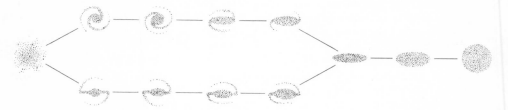

Fig. 5.9 Shapley's evolutionary sequence for galaxies.

This sequence of events in the evolution of a galaxy, while attractive, does have flaws which cannot be overlooked. Certain double galaxies, it may be assumed, have formed from the same cloud of gas and should, therefore, be the same age, much as are the stars in a star cluster. If this were so and Shapley's theory were correct, then such galaxies would be of the same type, but frequently they are not. Furthermore, could irregular galaxies develop into spiral galaxies with an attendant increase in mass? Then, too, spiral galaxies are extremely flat when seen edge-on and elliptical galaxies are never that flat. No mechanism has been discovered that would explain why a spiral galaxy would round out in this manner. It has been suggested that it is no more reasonable to expect a sequence of this type for the cycle of a galaxy than for the evolution of a star. The chances are that a galaxy forms into one type or another perhaps on the basis of its mass and angular momentum.

5.8   GALACTIC DISTANCES

Distances to objects within the solar system have long been known with a reasonable degree of accuracy. This is now of particular importance since man is planning to visit various bodies in the solar system. Distances to stars are measurable, but a need for accuracy is not nearly so critical. An error of a few million miles in the tremendous distances involved represents only a small percentage error, and since man does not contemplate so extensive a journey in the foreseeable future a need for greater accuracy is not required.

Measurement of distances to external galaxies is a relatively recent accomplishment, having been first successfully made in 1924. While the existence of external galaxies or "island universes" was suggested by Kant (Section 5.1) and subscribed to by many astronomers, the problem was not definitely solved until Edwin Hubble photographed the Andromeda nebula through the 100-inch telescope in 1924. Individual dots had been seen in Andromeda before this, as long ago as in 1889. However, it was thought that this indicated Andromeda was a part of the Milky Way since otherwise the dots would have to be giant star clusters or small galaxies in order to be seen at such great distances. Hubble's photographs revealed sharp pinpoints of light that were obviously stars of every type, some of which fluctuated in brightness and were identified as Cepheids. With such information and with the knowledge of the relationship of luminosity to period, Hubble made a first distance-determination from the Milky Way to Andromeda, 900,000 light-years. This clearly placed Andromeda in the realm of an external galaxy beyond the boundaries of the Milky Way. Hubble also made a study of the frequent novae that occurred—130 in a few years—and this confirmed the identity of Andromeda as a galaxy. He made use of the novae as a means of measuring distances to about 100 other galaxies in which he was able to detect individual stars.

Distances to galaxies are even more difficult to measure than was originally thought because of the complicating factor of interstellar dust and gas. This caused Hubble to err in his first determination, but the techniques he developed were of great value since they provided the means of measuring such distances. He made the same assumption that is made by all other physical scientists, namely, that all the laws of nature which operate on earth or in the stellar vicinity of the earth, apply to all other areas of the universe both in space and in time. Hubble assumed that the luminosity-period relationship that existed for Cepheids in the Milky Way applied to the Cepheids wherever they could be seen. This method has proved to be the most reliable one yet found for measuring intergalactic distances. The luminosity of a Cepheid is related to the period of pulsation (Section 4.10), and this relationship is well established. The length of the period can be measured; the absolute magnitude can be determined; and finally the distance can be calculated. Unfortunately, the distance to which this method can be applied is limited to about 20 million light-years. Within this radius only about 30 galaxies with resolvable Cepheids are found, although up to 150 galaxies are visible.

Other methods were developed as equipment and techniques improved and more stars were resolved. Particularly bright stars (red giants and blue giants) were useful in checking the results obtained with Cepheids. The brightness of novae and supernovae has also been of value to a limited extent, but as yet there are insufficient data on their characteristics to make them a reliable means of measuring distances.

The use of resolvable stars as a means of measuring intergalactic distances is quite limited and does not yield data for the very faint galaxies. The intrinsic brightness of the galaxies themselves may be used, but it is difficult to know whether an isolated galaxy is a nearby dim one or a very distant bright one. Only when it is compared with neighboring galaxies can some concept of its brightness be obtained. At present this type of data can be used only in a theoretical, statistical way to give some clue as to the distance of a group of remote galaxies. Many more data must be available to make this a reliable method.

Certain problems plagued the astronomers after Hubble's first values were presented in the 1920's. The Milky Way, for example, appeared to be two to three times larger than any other galaxy in the visible universe. Why this was so was a mystery. Furthermore, novae in the Milky Way appeared to be of a different type from those in neighboring galaxies, and the globular clusters in the Milky Way were brighter than those in the Andromeda galaxy. The influence of interstellar dust and gas on light was gradually recognized, and distances both within the Milky Way and from the Milky Way to external galaxies were corrected. It was not until 1952 with the aid of the 200-inch telescope that an error in the values calculated for the magnitude and distance of the

Cepheids was discovered. An adjustment equivalent to a factor of 4 in luminosity had to be made. This meant that an object that was in reality four times brighter than originally thought must be not only twice as far away but twice as large in order to have the observed apparent magnitude. Thus, the Andromeda galaxy is approximately 2 million light-years from earth and twice as large as previously judged, making it in fact slightly larger than the Milky Way.

One other indirect method of measuring distance makes use of the red-shift phenomenon described in Section 2.5. V. M. Slipher first used this technique in the early part of the twentieth century to measure velocities of more than 40 "nebulae." He was unaware of the true nature of these objects but was able to measure velocities of up to 100 miles per second for these nebulae, most of which were moving away from the earth. During the 1920's these objects were identified as galaxies, and some evidence indicated that there was a relationship between the velocity and the distance of the galaxy from the earth. Hubble, in the course of his other studies and in collaboration with M. Humason, was able to ascertain by 1930 that the speed with which galaxies receded was in direct proportion to their distance from the earth. This phenomenon became known as the *red shift law*. Since 1949 work by Humason with the 200-inch telescope has confirmed the value of this law. He was able to establish a velocity of recession of 38,000 miles per second at a distance of 2.6 billion light-years for one of the remote Hydra clusters. By 1963 the greatest velocity measured was for a galaxy in the handle of Ursa Major. The red shift here implied a velocity of 86,000 miles per second or about 45% of the speed of light. In 1965 a form of quasar which emits no radio waves and which is called a blue stellar object was detected by A. Sandage and M. Schmidt. This object was found to be moving away from the earth at a velocity of 125,000 miles per second. At the same time quasar 3C–9, the most distant object from earth, had also been found to be receding from the earth at approximately 149,000 miles per second or at about 80% of the speed of light.

Accurate distances cannot as yet be determined by using the red shift. However, some indication of distance may be obtained from the following relationship:

$$r = \frac{V}{H},$$

where r is the distance to the remote galaxy, V is the velocity of recession, and H is a value known as *Hubble's constant*. This constant, although not accurate, expresses the increase in the rate of recession of distant galaxies per unit of distance, and for purposes here, may be given as an increase of 15 miles per second for every million light-years from the earth. This value was obtained by plotting the velocities of distant galaxies against the distances, where the distances could be established by other methods.

Some astronomers doubt the validity of this relationship (speed of recession to distance) and feel that the red shift is the result of some effect on light moving through great distances in space. They attribute the cause of at least a part of the red shift to "a tiring of light as it moves through space" and argue that for this reason the total red shift should be adjusted downward in order to obtain a true velocity of recession. Since no experimental evidence has as yet been presented to support this theory, speed of recession as measured by red shift is accepted.

5.9 GALACTIC MOTION

The earth was taken as the reference point for measuring motion within the solar system despite the fact that the earth itself was moving. Similarly, the sun was used as a convenient reference point for measuring stellar motion. In the same way, the Milky Way may be used as a reference point for measuring galactic motion. To further complicate the calculations, allowance must be made for the fact that in all three cases observations are made from the moving earth.

Motion within the Milky Way results from the movement of individual stars revolving around a common center. As in the solar system, those bodies closer to the center revolve at a more rapid pace than those toward the rim of the galaxy. The resulting motion as seen from a neighboring galaxy would resemble a gigantic pinwheel slowly spinning in space. The same motion has been detected in other galaxies and appears to be common to all.

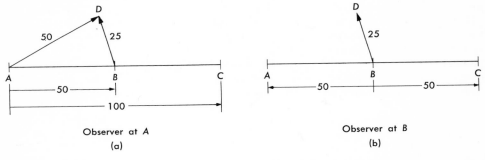

Fig. 5.10 Motion of galaxies with respect to each other in an expanding universe. Units are arbitrary.

The detection of motion of external galaxies through use of the red-shift phenomenon has resulted in some interesting ramifications. It appears from these studies that all but a few neighboring galaxies are moving away from the Milky Way. Regardless of the direction in which observations are made the result is the same—all galaxies appear to be receding, and the greater the distances the greater the velocity of recession. This movement gives the impression that the Milky Way is in the center of the universe, but an examination of Fig. 5.10 will quickly reveal that an observer at any point in the universe would see all galaxies receding. An observer on galaxy A (Fig. 5.10a) would see galaxy B moving away from himself at a rate of 50 units. The point that should be made here is that there is no way of knowing whether this apparent motion is the result of movement by galaxy A, galaxy B, or the net result of their combined motion. If Galaxy C were moving away from galaxy A at 100 units, an observer at B would see A receding at 50 units and C receding at 50 units. Galaxy D would be receding from galaxy A at 50 units, being the same distance from A that B is. Galaxy D, however, is closer to galaxy B therefore would be receding at a slower rate. The diagram depicts this motion in two dimensions only, but by picturing this in three dimensions, it is easy to see the nature of an expanding universe.

The element of time is an interesting aspect of galactic motion, particularly for the very distant galaxies. Light has a finite velocity which means that an expression of distance in light-years (or parsecs) implies time. Light coming from the galaxy in Hydra traveling at a velocity of 186,000 miles per second over a distance of 2.6 billion light-years requires 2.6 billion years to make the journey. The light seen at present is a record of conditions that existed 2.6 billion years ago. It must also be recalled that this galaxy was receding at a velocity of 38,000 miles per second. On an assumption that it has continued to do so during the past 2.6 billion years, the galaxy would now be more than 3 billion light-years from the earth, and light now leaving the stars within this very distant galaxy would not reach the earth for another 3 billion years.

5.10   DISTRIBUTION OF GALAXIES

The distribution of galaxies, first studied by Hubble using the 100-inch telescope, gives some indication of the structure of the universe. Hubble plotted the density of galaxies and found them to be more or less uniformly distributed over the sky except for an obscured region where viewing is blocked by the presence of the Milky Way. It was assumed that a similar distribution occurs in this region of the sky; this assumption has now been proved to be correct by the observation of galaxies through "windows" in the less dense portions of the obscured regions. Hubble was also able to show that doubling the observable distance by longer exposures through the telescope increased

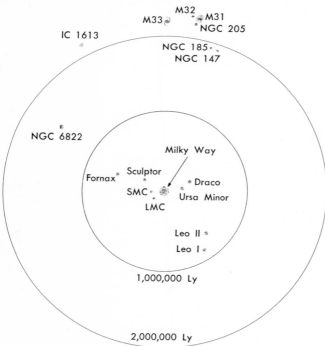

Fig. 5.11 Distribution of galaxies in the local group.

the number of galaxies seen in space by about 8 times. This corresponds to the fact that doubling the radius of a sphere increases the volume of the sphere by 8 times.

Detailed study has shown that galaxies are not independent "islands" but are associated in clusters or groups ranging from a few to thousands of galaxies acting in unison. The Milky Way is one of 17 galaxies that make up what is known as the Local Group. The Local Group is spread over a region of about 3 million light-years, as shown in Fig. 5.11. The positions are plotted on an arbitrary plane with the Milky Way set in the central position. From this point the galaxies in the Local Group are within a radius of slightly more than 2 million light-years from the Milky Way. Table 5.1 lists certain pertinent data on known members of the Local Group. Other galaxies may be present but obscured by the dust clouds of the Milky Way. In addition, certain galaxies that are thought to be small and dim because of great distance may be dwarflike and actually within the Local Group.

Many galactic clusters outside the Local Group have been observed and have provided valuable data in the study of luminosities, types, and sizes, because members of a particular cluster are substantially at the same distance and true relationships may be observed. Some clusters are quite rich in galaxies. The Coma cluster, for example, has about 500 galaxies in a region that is less than 50% larger than that occupied by the Local Group. Dense clusters of this type are of interest in that they contain few spiral galaxies. Many of the galaxies are described as armless spirals. The lack of arms has been attributed to collisions between galaxies. Such an event is not so cataclysmic as it appears. Stars and

TABLE 5.1   THE LOCAL GROUP

Galaxy	*Distance (1000 light years)*	*Radial Velocity* (Miles per second)*	*Type*	*Mass (Solar masses)*
Milky Way	—	—	Sb	2×10^{11}
Large Magellanic Cloud, LMC	160	+171	Irr	2.5×10^{10}
Small Magellanic Cloud, SMC	180	+104	Irr	
Ursa Minor—dwarf	220		E4	
Sculptor—dwarf	270		E3	3×10^6
Draco—dwarf	330		E2	
Fornax—dwarf	600	+24	E3	1.5×10^7
Leo II—dwarf	750		E0	1.1×10^6
Leo I—dwarf	900		E4	
NGC 6822	1500	−20	Irr	
NGC 147	1900		E6	
NGC 185	1900	−190	E2	
NGC 205	2200	−149	E5	
M32 (NGC 221)	2200	−133	E3	
1C 1613	2200	−149	Irr	
Andromeda (M31) (NGC 224)	2200	−165	Sb	4×10^{11}
M33 (NGC 598)	2300	−117	Sc	8×10^9

* + indicates movement away from earth
  − indicates movement toward the earth

their attendant planets occupy only a tiny fraction of the total volume of a galaxy, so that collisions by individual stars in colliding galaxies are extremely remote. Gases within these galaxies are, however, swept out and since the arms of spirals are rich in dust, these arms are lost. Nor is a collision of this magnitude an instantaneous event. As long as 100,000 years may elapse between the onset of the collision and the separation of the galaxies.

The galactic cluster does not appear to be the largest organized entity in the universe. There are several thousand galaxies within a radius of about 70 million light-years, all organized into clusters of which the Virgo cluster is the largest. G. de Vancouleurs has found that beyond 70 million light-years there is a scarcity of galaxies for a considerable distance and that this local group of clusters constitutes a supercluster, or supergalaxy, 100 million light-years in diameter. He has suggested that the supergalaxy is organized into a flattened disk with the Virgo cluster at its center. The Milky Way lies near the plane of this structure about 40 million light-years from its center. Evidence also points to the possibility that the supergalaxy is rotating. Another example of a supergalaxy appears in Hercules, where several clusters appear to be overlapping.

5.11 RADIO GALAXIES

Radio waves, like light waves, are a part of the electromagnetic spectrum. They differ only in wave-length, so it is reasonable to assume that celestial objects which emit light and heat also emit radio waves. An attempt was made at the turn of the century to detect such radio waves from the sun, but this was unsuccessful because of inadequate equipment. It was not until the 1930's that such an attempt was successful. Since that time a new branch of astronomy has developed in which the universe is viewed through the medium of radio waves instead of light waves. This enables astronomers to study invisible as well as visible sources of energy.

At first it appeared that radio waves originated only within the Milky Way, but soon it became evident that external sources also were responsible for invisible radiation. Several sources were located in regions where no apparent object seemed to be located. Not until 1954 was Walter Baade, with the aid of the 200-inch telescope, able to identify visually a radio source discovered by Hey in England and Bolton and Stanley in Australia. The radio source coincided with the position of a pair of colliding galaxies in Cygnus. This object, now known as Cygnus A, located 700 million light-years from earth, is an energetic emitter of radio waves.

More than 100 discrete radio sources have been identified as coming from visible galaxies. These galaxies have been classified into two general groups, namely, the *normal* galaxies and the *peculiar* galaxies. Although there is no clear-cut distinction between them, the categories have been found useful. The normal galaxies include most of the spiral and irregular galaxies, both of which are weak radio emitters. The Andromeda galaxy is the first of the external galaxies from which radio emissions were detected. This is a normal galaxy and was so categorized in 1950 by Brown and Hazard on the basis of data they obtained with the aid of the 220-foot diameter Jodrell Bank radio telescope. Cygnus A is an example of a peculiar galaxy having strong radio emissions apparently resulting from the collision of two galaxies. Cygnus A has also been thought of as a galaxy whose nucleus is splitting into two galaxies. As yet no satisfactory hypothesis has been presented which explains to everyone's complete satisfaction the source of so much energy.

5.12 SUMMARY

The twentieth century has been a time of tremendous discovery in astronomy. Not only has the true nature of the Milky Way been revealed, but the existence of external galaxies has been verified. With the techniques now available, it is possible to estimate the distances and the mass of objects so far away that the light from these objects left its point of origin before life developed on earth. Much is known now about the structure of galaxies, and theories have been formulated on the possible mode of their evolution. Some clues based on the probable arrangement of the visible universe seem to indicate that the galaxy is not the ultimate structure. Evidence is available which hints at a "galaxy of galaxies" or supergalactic structure flattened into a disk and possibly rotating. Is it conceivable that further organization exists—a galaxy of supergalaxies? No data are available to confirm or deny this premise. Future studies will be directed toward securing more accurate and comprehensive data, proving or disproving existing theories, and theorizing further about the structure and the origin of the universe.

SUGGESTED READINGS

ABELL, G., *Exploration of the Universe.* New York: Holt, Rinehart and Winston, 1964.

BAADE, W., *Evolution of Stars and Galaxies.* Cambridge, Mass.: Harvard University Press, 1963.

SHAPLEY, H., *Galaxies,* rev. ed. Cambridge, Mass.: Harvard University Press, 1961.

WHITROW, G. J., *The Structure and Evolution of the Universe.* New York: Harper Torchbooks, 1959.

CHAPTER 6

THEORIES OF COSMOLOGY

Consideration of the arrangement of stars, galaxies, and supergalaxies within the visible universe leads to the question of how it all began. This text is not concerned with the Creation itself but rather with events which have occurred since that first moment. It is important to avoid the confusion that sometimes occurs in attempts to reconcile theology and science in a discussion of the origin of the universe. It should be clear that science attempts to answer questions such as What has been occurring? and How did it take place? Science attempts to trace the sequence of events from that very first moment. It is easy to interpret events in the recent past, but it becomes increasingly more difficult the further one delves into the past. Data are extremely scarce, and the scientist must extrapolate in order to understand events in distant time and space. The theologian, on the other hand, attempts to explain why the universe was created. He is involved in the problem of absolute beginnings and the reason for creation.

6.1 HISTORY OF COSMOLOGY

Cosmology, the science which deals with the evolution and organization of the universe, is of relatively recent origin, yet its roots go back to the ancient astronomers. More than 2000 years ago Chinese (Taoist) astronomers, attempting to describe the universe, developed the Hsuan Yeh or "Empty Infinite Space" theory. Previous Chinese theories had put limits on the universe, but according to Hsuan Yeh, space was empty and had no shape. It was occupied by the earth and other visible celestial bodies which were propelled by "hard winds" through an infinite space. Over the centuries the basic concept of empty infinite space was incorporated with other theories and eventually abandoned.

The Greek astronomer Aristarchus (ca. 280 B.C.) also suggested that space was not bounded by the sky containing the stars. He explained the lack of parallax of the stars by suggesting that they were an infinite distance from earth—a distance too great for parallax to be observed. He thus subscribed to what was to become the modern view of an infinite universe.

During the Renaissance a certain amount of speculation existed about the infinite nature of the universe. This was expressed by Nicolaus Cusanus (1401–1404), Bishop of Brixen, who felt that the heavens were of the same nature as the earth and were inhabited by earthlike creatures; the universe was infinite, and regardless of what position in the universe one occupied, it would appear as though that were the center and all else was in motion around it.

Perhaps the first true cosmologist was Giordano Bruno (1548–1600) who was neither an astronomer nor a scientist, but rather a philosopher. Wherever he went he invoked wild enthusiasm or bitter hatred by preaching the Copernican doctrine. Where Copernicus had replaced the earth by the sun as the center of the universe, Bruno went a step further, implying that the sun was a star among many stars in a boundless universe. He had no evidence to support this contention, and it would be several hundred years before sufficient data became available to prove him right. He described a universe filled with countless sun and planets, and predicated the possibility that these planets supported life. Bruno was far ahead of his time, and his ideas were not appreciated. Centuries passed before the full impact of his reasoning was felt and found valid.

Thomas Digges, a contemporary of Bruno's, reasoned along the same lines as Bruno. Digges, an early English translator and advocate of Copernicus' works, no longer felt bound by the sphere of fixed stars surrounding a central earth. He viewed the cosmos as a collection of stars all placed in an infinite universe at varying distances from a central sun.

The concept of infinite space was strengthened in the generations that followed Copernicus by the slow but continual expansion of knowledge. Kant, Wright, and Herschel first visualized the structure of the galaxy. Bessel was able to measure the enormous distances that separated even the nearby stars. A comprehensive view of the structure of the universe is only now beginning to take shape. On the basis of new information several important cosmological theories have been formulated. These differ primarily in the interpretation given to the recession of distant galaxies as measured by the red shift law which would indicate an expanding universe.

6.2   THE EVOLUTIONARY UNIVERSE

Georges Lemaître, a Belgian astronomer, is credited with first enunciating the evolutionary theory. His proposal, published in 1931, considered that the universe originated as an extremely dense (100 million tons per cubic centimeter) hot mass which he called the *atome primitif* which, translated, means primeval atom, now commonly called primeval nucleus. This mass contained all the matter in the universe and had a diameter of about 200 million miles, or about the diameter of the earth's orbit. This volume was obtained from what was thought to be the average density of the universe and from Einstein's estimate of the diameter of the universe. This mass exploded, according to Lemaître, and the particles which he called "atom stars" were scattered at high velocity in all directions. The matter continued to expand, thinning out, cooling, and emitting radioactive particles during the process. Lemaître suggested that during this period the heavier elements were formed. He believed that elements such as uranium with long half-lives have retained their radioactive character.

Lemaître believed that the universe, at that very early moment, was restricted to the boundaries of the primeval nucleus and that nothing existed beyond this. When the initial explosion took place, the universe began to expand at a rate equal to the velocity of the fragments from the primeval nucleus. With expansion, there was a decrease in density of the matter scattered in space. The particles, however, maintained their mass and therefore exerted a gravitational force. This gravitational force gradually slowed down the rate of expansion until after a few billion years expansion practically ceased, and the universe was in a state of relative equilibrium. The universe became nearly static, a condition already described by Einstein where the forces of expansion and gravity are in balance. It was during this phase that the galaxies began to form by the condensation of matter. During this stage there was considerable unstability.

After several billion years the forces of expansion overcame the gravitational forces, and the universe resumed its expansion, a state which is continuing today. What will

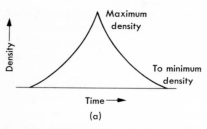
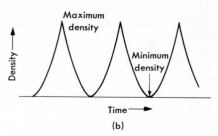

Fig 6.1 Models of the universe: (a) hyperbolic, and (b) pulsating.

be the ultimate fate of the universe? This depends upon whether or not intergalactic space contains any matter. If little or no matter exists in the space between galaxies then, according to the Lemaître theory, the expansion of the universe will continue until the density approaches zero. This model of the universe has been described as a *hyperbolic* universe, one in which matter originally existed in an extremely rarefied state, then contracted into a dense compact mass which exploded and is again expanding toward the point of minimum density (Fig. 6.1a). On the other hand, if the matter present in intergallactic space is equal to seven times the mass of the galaxies, a *pulsating* universe exists. In this model the universe would alternately expand and contract from maximum density to minimum density in a continuous cycle (Fig. 6.1b). Only in recent years has evidence of intergalactic dust and gas been found and then only within the confines of supergalaxies. As yet no quantitative determinations have been possible, and until such are made the question of whether the universe is hyperbolic or pulsating cannot be answered.

How old the universe is is another question that cannot be easily answered. Lemaître hypothesized that the universe has passed through three stages of development: the initial stage of expansion from the primeval nucleus, the period of equilibrium during which the galaxies were formed, and the subsequent period of expansion of the universe. Retracing the history of the galaxies—by theoretically reversing the process so that the universe would be shrinking rather than expanding—made it possible to determine how long ago the equilibrium conditions existed when the galaxies were first being formed. This period, when first calculated, covered several billion years and accounted for only that stage during which the galaxies were receding from one another. It is not possible to establish a time scale for the period during which the universe was in equilibrium or for the initial stage of expansion from the primeval nucleus. The time that elapsed between the explosion of the primeval nucleus and the formation of the galaxies has been estimated at 20 to 60 billion years.

Lemaître's theory faced many problems after it was first presented. For example, the age of the universe as measured by the recession of the galaxies was established at slightly less than 2 billion years. This figure was contradicted by the discovery of rocks on the earth which were in excess of 3 billion years old. The problem was resolved with Baade's discovery in 1952 that the magnitude of Cepheids had been underestimated and that distances to the galaxies were more than twice what they had been thought to be. This raised the possible age of the universe to 5 billion years and disposed of the apparent contradiction. Discoveries in the past few years have further extended this age to almost 13 billion years.

Lemaître's theory was not the only version of the evolution of the universe. This theory was important from a historical standpoint, however, because it was the first cosmological theory based on observations of the behavior of the universe. Previous presentations were philosophical or mathematical in nature. In 1946 George Gamow proposed a modified form of the evolutionary theory, and this form is one of the two theories currently being given serious consideration. Gamow's theory differed in several respects from Lemaître's theory.

In Gamow's universe, the very dense state of matter of *ylem,* as Gamow refers to it, is essentially gaseous with radiant energy predominant. At this initial stage, before expansion began, the matter was composed of protons, neutrons, and electrons. Five minutes after expansion began, the mass was cool enough that hydrogen and the heavier elements could be formed from the protons, neutrons, and electrons. This process continued for about 30 minutes when the temperature became too cool for these reactions to continue. Within an hour after expansion started the universe had cooled to 250 million degrees, and in 200,000 years to the temperature of the sun's surface. By the time the universe was 250 million years old, the temperature had dropped to 100 degrees below the freezing point for water. This particular point is important in Gamow's theory. It was at this time that the gravitational effect of matter began to dominate the effect of radiant energy because in the expanding process, the density of radiant energy decreased faster than did the density of matter. Gas clouds separated from one another as the universe continued to expand, and these chaotic gas clouds condensed and formed the galaxies.

Gamow's theory also differs from Lemaître's in the effect of the initial explosion of matter. According to Lemaître, the universe came to a resting state or state of equilibrium and expansion continued only after the galaxies were formed. In Gamow's theory, the galaxies were formed at a given period without a discontinuance of expansion. Expansion has continued unabated from the very moment of that initial explosion.

The fact that the expansion does take place and did start at some point in the distant past is a feature both the Lemaître and Gamow theories have in common. There is also the implication of an "all in one" creation at some remote moment.

What lies beyond the evolutionary universe? The best answer may be nothing. Space, as usually recognized, may not exist since space implies measurement and direction. There is no point to measure from or to, nor is there a frame of reference for measuring direction or motion. The same may be said for time which exists only as a measure for the spacing of events. No events of any type are seen to be occurring, therefore time as a dimension does not exist.

6.3 THE STEADY-STATE THEORY

In 1948, Thomas Gold, Hermann Bondi, and Fred Hoyle of England proposed another cosmological theory. They suggested that creation is a continuing process and that hydrogen is continually being formed. The main point of this theory is that the universe is essentially unchanging. The features a billion years ago are much the same as they are now and will be a billion years in the future. The overall population of galaxies does not change, although the individual components do. This idea was based on a "cosmological principle" first suggested by Bondi and Gold, namely, that the universe is unchanging in space and in time. From whatever point in space or time an observer views

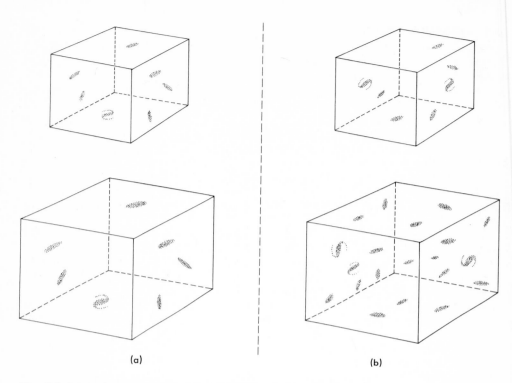

(a)

(b)

Fig. 6.2 (a) Evolutionary universe and (b) steady-state universe.

the universe, it shows the same general features. This implies a steady state, a state of continuous being without change (Fig. 6.2). But the universe is in motion and galaxies are receding in all directions.

How is it possible to maintain a continuous steady state in which any portion of the universe will maintain the same population of galaxies over extended periods of time? This is where the continuous creation of hydrogen plays an important role in the theory. As galaxies move out of range, new galaxies are formed from the spontaneously created hydrogen to replace them. The assumption is made that hydrogen is formed at a rate sufficient to replace and maintain the density of the galactic population. Individual galaxies are born, evolve through their life cycle, and gradually fade out as the stars become black dwarfs and die. If such be the case, there are, in any locale in space, old and young galaxies in about the same proportions.

Hoyle best describes this concept by comparing the universe to a settlement of humans. From a distance, it is possible to distinguish the old, middle-aged, and young who inhabit the town and make up the total population. Assuming no change in population, the old die and are replaced by the birth of new individuals so that if the settlement were viewed 100 years later it would appear unchanged except for the difference in individuals. The universe, according to Hoyle, has existed in this manner for an infinitely long time, is infinitely large, and has neither end nor beginning.

6.4 DISCUSSION OF THE TWO MAIN THEORIES

In addition to describing the basic tenets of the evolutionary and steady-state theories, it may be profitable also to compare their similarities and differences and discuss some of the problems which the proponents of these theories face.

One of the features that both theories have in common concerns the creation of matter. The evolutionary theory proposes that creation took place all at one time and since then no new matter has been formed. The steady-state theory holds that matter in the form of hydrogen has been and is being formed spontaneously and continuously throughout the entire universe. This concept has been objected to by proponents of the evolutionary theory because it is inconceivable to them that something, in a sense, can be formed from nothing. Those who support the steady-state theory feel there is no difference between assuming that all matter was formed at one time and that matter is being formed continuously. The difference lies not in the fact of creation but in when creation occurs.

Another feature both theories recognize is the fact of the expanding universe. The evolutionary theory reasons back from this fact to predicate the initial explosion of matter and energy, causing it to expand at high speed in all directions. With time the density of matter would constantly decrease until at some future time the density of the universe would approach zero. The proponents of the steady-state theory also recognize the expansion of the universe. However, in the steady-state universe expansion does not result in a decrease in density. The formation of new hydrogen and the subsequent formation of new galaxies would maintain a static population of galaxies.

A study of the differences between the two theories will ultimately prove one or the other or both theories to be incorrect. One of the differences already mentioned is the change or lack of change in density resulting from the expansion of the universe. If the density decreases, it would imply the correctness of the evolutionary theory which states that no new matter is being created to replace that which is receding outward. By the same token, if the density of the universe remains uniform, it would be evidence in favor of the steady-state theory. Can a change in density be detected? Not in a short period of time, but it must be recalled that distant galaxies are seen as they were 1 or 2 or 5 billion years ago. Those galaxies 5 billion light-years away would appear as they did 5 billion years ago, and they could be compared with the galaxies in the immediate vicinity of the Milky Way. This is easier said than done. Galaxies at those great distances have been detected only within the last decade. Measuring densities at those distances is not an easy task.

Another cosmological test is that of the ages of galaxies. If, in accordance with the evolutionary theory, all matter (and therefore galaxies) were formed at approximately the same time, it may be concluded that all galaxies are the same age. Since an observer looks further backward into time as he peers farther out into space, the more distant galaxies should appear younger. Under conditions of steady state, the galaxies are born, mature, and die so that galaxies of all ages should exist side by side. The very distant galaxies would therefore not appear any different with respect to age than those nearby. Again, the problem is not easily solved in that the techniques for determining the age of individual galaxies are not as yet too satisfactory.

Other problems must be satisfactorily resolved before either theory can be completely acceptable. The steady-state theory appears to be in conflict with the law of conservation of energy which states that energy can neither be created nor destroyed, only changed from one form to another. The continuous creation of hydrogen violates this law, but Hoyle states that this activity must be viewed on the basis of the differences between a closed system, which may be considered to include only the conditions on earth, and an open system, encompassing the entire universe. Creation within any limited volume of space would be extremely small, perhaps on the order of one hydrogen atom per 1000 years in an average-size room. This rate of change would not be measurable even over an extended period of time, so for practical purposes the law of conservation of energy would not be violated within the scope of human experience on earth. In the universe itself, a certain energy is utilized in the expansion process and as expansion takes place beyond the confines of any given volume of space, new matter is created to replace that which has left, thus maintaining a balance and preserving the spirit of the law of conservation of energy.

At this point a question may be asked with respect to the creation of hydrogen. Is matter in the form of hydrogen truly created or is it formed by the conversion of energy (light for example) into matter under conditions found in intergalactic space by a process as yet unknown? Matter is converted into energy within the stars. Is it not possible that the process is reversed in the cold darkness of outer space? Such a concept would not only "save" the law of conservation of energy but would also signify a finite limit on the amount of energy and matter in the universe. It would preserve the steady-state universe in that new galaxies continue to be born, but at a decreasing rate, with the passage of time. Matter would be "locked up" in the black dwarfs of dying galaxies, causing the eventual demise of the entire universe. This idea is in keeping with a portion of the evolutionary-universe theory which, while it does not envision the rebirth of galaxies, does imply the ultimate death of the universe.

One of the arguments against the evolutionary theory is the preponderance of hydrogen in the universe. Measurements of matter in the universe indicate that approximately 92% of all the atoms in the universe are hydrogen and over 6% are helium. The high amount of hydrogen can be explained on the basis of spontaneous creation and is a necessary adjunct to the steady-state theory. If the elements were formed in the first few minutes after the universe began to evolve, or as Gamow stated, "in less time than it takes to roast duck and potatoes," why was so much hydrogen left over after this initial stage? Also, if hydrogen is the main fuel for stars, why was such a small amount used at the time the galaxies first formed? The presence of so much hydrogen has been used by the steady-state protagonists to support their theory. They contend that the hydrogen was formed at some finite time and continues to be created and utilized in the formation of new galaxies.

Recent evidence to support the theory that the heavy elements are formed within and during the life cycle of the stars has also cast doubt on the phase of the evolutionary theory dealing with the formation of these elements. This is not to say that these elements could not have formed in the manner outlined in the evolutionary theory since there are similarities between the two methods. Element formation within the stars, while not a certainty, is supported by evidence that makes the steady-state theory a better prospect than the evolutionary theory. Some cosmologists, however, feel that the evolutionary theory has merit because of the very fact of evolution in nature. To them evolution appears to be a basic law of nature—a process whereby nature changes according to a given pattern.

Which theory will win out depends on the results of continued observation and measurement. Many technical problems must be overcome. The interference presented by the atmosphere has been eliminated in part by the use of radio telescopes. Perhaps the establishment of satellite observatories or an observatory on the moon, where atmospheric disturbances and distortions are minimal, will bring the problem of the origin of the universe closer to a final resolution.

6.5   LIFE IN THE UNIVERSE

No discourse in astronomy would be complete without a discussion of the prospect of the existence of some form of life in outer space. When the spectrograph was first developed astronomers viewed its possibilities enthusiastically and anticipated many new discoveries. It was soon found that other stars even in other galaxies were made up of essentially the same material as the sun, and that the construction of the universe was amazingly uniform. No elements were discovered in very distant galaxies which did not occur in the solar system. Temperatures and pressures of stars, while varying from those of the sun, obeyed the same physical laws that controlled the activity of the sun. Under these circumstances it would not be surprising if life occurred in other parts of the universe. In fact, it would be surprising if it did not.

Life is generally described in terms of those forms found on earth. It is based on carbon, a very versatile element, which has the capacity to combine with other elements, notably oxygen and hydrogen, in a tremendous array of molecules. Water is essential as both a solvent and a medium in which the many complex reactions within the organism can take place. These elements along with the other elements necessary for life are quite commonplace in the universe. This does not mean that life is dependent on the presence of these specific elements. It is possible that some life form may have evolved in some distant place based on chlorine or silicon instead of carbon, since these elements are almost as versatile. However, there is no evidence to support such an idea, so it is necessary to limit the discussion to the requirements of a carbon-based form of life.

Life, as it exists on the earth today, is adapted to a variety of environments and conditions. It is possible to establish some environmental conditions that must be met in order for life as we know it to exist. Aside from the presence of the essential elements (and this may be assumed since these elements are universally present), conditions conducive to the development and continuance of life include a moderate temperature ranging from about 20°F to 140°F. Chemical activity is very sluggish at the lower end of the scale since pure water freezes at 32°F. The presence of salts in water will lower the freezing point and therefore permit some activity down to a temperature of about 20°F. At the upper end of the temperature range, certain molecules important to life break down when temperatures reach much above 140°F. Most life forms can tolerate temperatures outside these limits but only for limited periods of time. Man has been able to survive greater extremes because of his ability to modify his environment to suit his needs.

On the basis of temperature it is possible to establish the so-called life zone within the solar system. This is a zone ranging from Venus to Mars wherein temperatures on planets may be sufficiently tolerable to sustain life. In terms of the physical characteristics of the planets it is then possible to eliminate Mercury as being too hot or too cold for life to survive, much less develop. Of the other planets only Venus and Mars are within the limits of a zone where life is possible. Venus has a cloud layer which may entrap heat close to the surface making life insupportable. Only Mars, on the outer edge of the life zone, appears to have the prerequisites for some form of life. Temperatures are somewhat more rigorous than on earth, but are within tolerable limits for life. Mars has an atmosphere much rarer than earth's and lacks sufficient oxygen for animal life, but it is satisfactory for some forms of plant life. The Martian atmosphere contains up to ten times the carbon dioxide found in the atmosphere of the earth, a compound necessary for plant life at least on earth. Life on Mars, if in fact it has developed, will be adapted to conditions of low moisture, low temperature, and low atmospheric pressure. Lichens, which grow under rigorous conditions, have been tested in a simulated Martian environment and survived. While lichens may not be found, plant life similar to this is now thought to exist on Mars.

One other celestial body, the moon, is found within the limits of the life zone. The moon lacks an atmosphere and, for this reason, temperatures may be too extreme for life to have developed. For this reason great care is taken to sterilize lunar probes so that no earthlike organisms will contaminate the moon surface before studies can be made to determine whether life exists there.

Beyond Mars, the planets are too far from the sun to receive sufficient heat for life to evolve. Temperatures are far below freezing, being at most $-200°F$ on Jupiter and lower still on the planets beyond Jupiter. If the temperatures of these planets were not low enough to preclude life, their poisonous atmospheres would do so. These atmospheres, made up primarily of methane, ammonia, and hydrogen are extremely toxic to existing life forms on earth, although it is suspected that the atmosphere of the earth was once made up of these gases.

From all that can be observed, it appears that life within the solar system is confined to the earth; at least this may be said of intelligent life. The possibility that some form of primitive plantlike life exists on Mars may be confirmed in the near future. Extreme temperatures and hostile atmospheres have in all probability inhibited the development of life on other planets or satellites in the solar system.

Does life exist beyond the solar system? This question cannot be answered positively because of the tremendous distances to even the nearest stars. Even with the finest equipment presently available it is not possible to see planets associated with these stars, and it is unlikely that these stars will be visited in the foreseeable future. All that can be done at present is to speculate on the possibilities of life based on the existing knowledge of conditions associated with the various types of stars. The tremendous number of stars in the universe, more than 10^{20}, permits ample opportunities for the duplication of conditions similar to those which exist in our solar system. The fact that the chemistry of the universe is no different from that within the solar system, and the assumption that the same physical laws apply in all parts of the universe gives cause for believing that this duplication may occur many times.

In 1930 Sir James Jeans described the occurrence of life on earth as an accident of nature. According to Jeans, space was extremely cold and the stars too hot to support life. The fact that such an "accident" occurred was due to the extreme vastness of space and the long period of time during which it existed. Sir James quoted Huxley who said that if six monkeys were set to typing continuously for millions of years, they would in that time write all the books in the British Museum purely by chance. Although there has been a change in thinking on how often such an "accident" may occur, the present feeling is that planetary systems are quite commonplace and that life on at least a small percentage of these planets is possible.

Although a planet may be associated with a star and be within the life zone, there is no assurance that intelligent life would exist there. Life forms are assumed to progress up the evolutionary path from lower forms to higher forms over an extended period of time, perhaps 2 to 3 billion years. If the current theories of star evolution are correct, then some stars do not have a sufficiently long life cycle to permit life to develop. Type-O and Type-B stars (Table 4.2) are bright hot stars which have a short life cycle —too short to permit life to evolve to any fair degree on planets which may be associated with them. This is true also of Type-A and possibly early Type-F stars. These stars are adequately luminous so that even a planet with a slightly elliptical orbit would fall within the life zone. By the same token, stars of Type M and those lower on the main sequence have such a limited life zone, because of their small size, that only a planet with a perfectly circular orbit would be capable of supporting life. It is rather unlikely that planets achieve such an orbit, thus eliminating these stars as likely prospects. This narrows down the field of main sequence stars capable of having a large enough life zone and a long enough life cycle to Types late F, G, and early K. The sun, it will be recalled, is a Type-G-2 star.

Of the three dozen stars located within a radius of 5 parsecs of the sun, only a few are of these types. Epsilon Eridani is a Type K-2, located 3.3 parsecs from the sun, and Tau Ceti, a G-8 type, is 3.64 parsecs from the sun. The balance of the sun's neighbors are mostly M-type stars or are multiple star systems where planets are either unlikely to occur or have orbits too elliptical to remain within the life zone.

Approximately one-third of the stars in the neighborhood of the sun are members of multiple star systems. G. P. Kuiper has expressed the opinion that planetary systems are merely variations of the multiple star systems. If the angular momentum of the original dust and gas cloud is high, the cloud probably splits into two more or less equal masses to form a binary star. A smaller angular momentum results in one large and one small star, while a still smaller angular momentum may result in the star and a series of planets made up of 10% or less of the total mass. A very low speed of rotation results in a disk around a star, with a density too low to form planets. Studies of this phenomenon indicate that about 1% of the stars could have planetary systems. Some astronomers, however, believe that this figure may be as high as 10%.

What would this mean in terms of actual numbers of planets capable of supporting life? The total number of stars in the Milky Way is estimated to be about 100 billion. If only 1% of these have planetary systems, there is still a sizable number of them, something on the order of one billion. Obviously not all the planets associated with these stars are inhabited, because they would have to be located within the life zone and have sufficient mass to retain an atmosphere. Within the solar system three planets are in the life zone and seven have atmospheres. If this is typical of other systems, then many planets exist and are capable of sustaining some form of life.

Although life may exist in other parts of the universe, it is not necessarily as advanced as that found on earth. At the same time, if the star is a billion years or so older than the sun, a much more advanced type of civilization may exist. If this is the case, is it possible that the earth has been visited by beings from outer space at some time in the past? Such an idea would have been thought impossible a generation ago, but since then it has been suggested that life on earth resulted from the dumping of refuse from a visiting space vehicle. While such a contingency is considered extremely unlikely, it does raise the question of whether a voyage of this magnitude is possible. Epsilon Eridani, a star likely to have planets in the life zone, is 3.3 parsecs (10.8 light-years) from the earth. Even if speeds of $\frac{1}{100}$ that of light could be attained, the round trip would take more than 200 years. If man were to make such a voyage, it would stretch over several generations and, in fact, some would live their entire life span in space. Such a voyage from earth is impossible in the foreseeable future with our present technology, but this does not mean it will be forever impossible.

For the present, man is satisfied that initiating physical contact with a distant civilization is impossible, but some astronomers are attempting to communicate with other beings. Communication is possible with the equipment now available. A project in progress at the National Radio Astronomy Observatory in West Virginia is attempting to detect artificial signals from Tau Ceti which would indicate some intelligent control of the signals. The type of signals that could be expected would be the simplest form of abstraction involving basic numbers. Great patience is required since the minimum time between sending a message to Tau Ceti and receiving an answer, provided it is returned immediately, is over 20 years. However, the patience required would be well rewarded, for an achievement of this type would be one of the most important scientific events in human history.

If the presence of some form of intelligence can be established, it would be natural to speculate on the nature of the creatures that had sent the signals. There is no way of knowing what direction evolution may have taken on some other planet, but certain physical characteristics are essential to a creature possessing the intelligence necessary to communicate. The creature must possess a high degree of mobility, in order to gather raw materials necessary for communication equipment, and a high degree of manipulative ability to convert these materials into a usable form. This would imply some form of structure having features similar to human hands and legs. Since communication equipment and all equipment necessary for its functioning is complex, the creature would require vision and hearing. Many biologists believe that for the purpose of balance such alien organisms will possess a degree of symmetry such as is found in life on the earth. This would mean that intelligent forms may not be entirely dissimilar to man. Some scientists, however, feel that man is unique in the universe and that intelligent creatures on other planets are so unlike the humans on earth that they could not be classified on the same basis.

6.6   SUMMARY

Man has developed the science of astronomy from a limited universe in which he placed the earth at the center, to the infinite universe where the earth revolves around one of many billions of stars located near the outer edge of one of many billions of galaxies. From the very beginning, man has sought an explanation and proposed many theories. Even in ancient times many of these theories described the universe in terms of infinite space. This thinking has culminated in the current concepts of the evolutionary universe and the steady-state universe. Both theories have risen from essentially the same observations—observations which have been interpreted in different ways. Additional data and tests of existing data will aid in determining the validity of one or the other theory or lead to formulation of new theories.

Life forms on other planets have also been a subject of study in recent years. Until recently man in the universe was thought to be unique to the earth. Now that man's environmental needs and tolerances are better understood, and more is known about the nature of stars and planetary systems, it becomes evident that there is a good statistical possibility of some form of life on distant planets. Direct evidence to support such ideas is not available, and communication with other life-forms has not been established. With present technology there is little possibility of visiting some distant planet outside the solar system and discovering a new form of life. But man's capacity for solving problems is boundless, and ultimately his exploration of space will be bounded only by the time barrier.

SUGGESTED READINGS

BONDI, H., *Cosmology*, 2nd ed. New York: Cambridge University Press, 1960.
GAMOW, G., *The Creation of the Universe*, rev. ed. New York: Viking Press, 1961.
HOYLE, F., *The Nature of the Universe*. Oxford: B. Blackwell, 1960.
SCIAMA, D. W., *The Unity of the Universe*. New York: Doubleday, 1959.
SULLIVAN, W., *We Are Not Alone*. New York: McGraw-Hill, 1964.

INDEX

BCDE79876543210